The Mouse Hunter

by Lucile Hasley

SHEED AND WARD · NEW YORK · 1953

49023

D1363920

BS 3515.A8
H35 m

Library of Congress Catalog Card Number 53-9799
Manufactured in the United States of America

TO MY MOTHER

ACKNOWLEDGMENTS

Grateful acknowledgment is hereby made for the kind permission of the respective editors to reprint as follows:

THE SIGN: "Charlotte Mary Josephine," "Mother Wins Her Wings," "House of Light," "Swing Low, Sweet Chariot," "The Name is Susan," "There Must be an Easier Way," "Gather at the River," "The Little Girls."

THE MESSENGER OF THE SACRED HEART: "The Mouse Hunter."

THE MARIANIST: "Elizabeth."

MADEMOISELLE: "The Milestone" (copyright Street & Smith Publications, Inc., 1943).

COR: "I Remember Mama."

AVE MARIA: All selections in the section "Dibs and Dabs."

THE PRIEST: "Feelings Don't Count."

THE CATHOLIC INTERRACIALIST: "And How Are You Today?"

INTEGRITY: "Load that Plate, Lift that Fork."

THE VINCENTIAN: "Jeanmaire, Jeanmaire!"

WOMAN'S DAY: "May I Now Present?"

THE MISSIONARY SERVANT: "The Written Word," "I Fling the Torch."

MODERN SCREEN: Quotations from "How the Stars Found Faith" by Jane Powell (reprinted by permission of Dell Publishing Company, Inc.).

LITTLE, BROWN & CO.: Quotation from *Poems by Emily Dickinson,* edited by Martha Dickinson Bianchi and Alfred Leete Hampson.

PANTHEON BOOKS, Inc.: Quotations from the works of Charles Péguy.

CONTENTS

SHORT STORIES:

Essays

Charlotte Mary Josephine

L IKE GEORGE JESSEL, I always call my mother "Mama."
Only I don't very often get the chance to ring her up on
the phone ("That you, Mama? This is your Georgie. How you
feeling, Mama?") because it just so happens that she lives in
the same house with me.

This worse-than-death catastrophe took place eight years
ago and was one of the few times in my life when I've seen
my mother go to pieces. It was very flattering. "No!" she
wept, as if she were facing a stretch at Alcatraz instead of
moving in with her one and only daughter. "No! I want to be
independent! I don't want to be a burden! I want to die with
my boots on!"

This would have sounded very pathetic if only it hadn't
been so laughable. I mean, the idea that any living creature
could possibly make my mother take off her boots until she
was good and ready. Or that she would ever, barring a broken
hip or some other Act of God, permit herself to be a burden
to anyone. Even with her hip suspended in a pulley from the

ceiling and with both arms in casts, I daresay she would figure out *some* way to defray expenses. (Possibly by hatching eggs? I once read about a bedfast gentleman who, out of sheer boredom, started hatching Plymouth Rock chickens under his blankets. Ended up with a very tidy little profit, too.)

Yet it wasn't so much the horror of becoming a liability that haunted my mother, during that teary scene of eight years ago, as the more immediate horror of Two Women In One Kitchen. "Two women in one kitchen," she sobbed, "just never works out. Never has, never will."

Historically speaking, this is not quite accurate. I understand, as a matter of fact, that in many primitive villages in India the many-women-over-one-kettle-system is still in operation. Whether it's a truly happy arrangement for all concerned, I wouldn't know. All I know is that the natives of India—who are also used to famine, droughts, pestilence, and volcanic eruptions—are noted for their passive stoicism.

In America, the passive stoicism is not so noticeable. Two-women-over-one-kettle would be a marvellous theme (and a welcome one, I might add, after all the two-women-over-one-man variations) for a modern psychological novel: brimming over with female friction and frustration. It would also serve as a perfect motive for a murder mystery. The only element of mystery, however, would not so much be *why* the one woman killed the other (possibly an argument over whether milk bottles should be washed first or last) as *why* it hadn't happened sooner.

Yet murder, even though there is a certain admirable finality about it, is not the only way out of a difficult situation, and I figured that what was good enough for the Duke of Windsor was good enough for me. Abdication. Little did my mother realize that her unselfish daughter would be only too willing to step out of the kitchen and retire, with the typewriter she loved, to the living room.

My mother's sobs lessened as I promised that she, as the Queen Bee in the Hasley kitchen, could arrange and rearrange the kitchen cupboards to her heart's delight. I also urged her to feel perfectly free to wash all the dishes and do all the baking and put up all the canning that struck her fancy. She could even, I said, rising to great heights of heroic abandonment, defrost the refrigerator and carry out the garbage whenever she felt the urge.

I have kept my troth. I have never prevented my mother, or anyone else, for that matter, from making life easier for me. It is one of the few virtues—this allowing others to be virtuous—that come easy to me. It also answers the question that puzzled housewives most often ask me: "With three children, *how* do you find the time to sit down to the typewriter?" The idea that I'm a ball of fire around the house never seems to enter their heads. They seem to feel, and how right they are, that I have a secret weapon that I'm keeping under cover.

"Mama," I said the other day, "the time has come to reveal you. Would you mind very much if I stuck you into an essay?"

She looked at me as if I'd suggested sticking her into a kiln. "Oh, no, you don't!" she said, with all of her usual indecisiveness. "I know *you* and the way you exaggerate things to high heaven. You'd probably make me sound like a character in a book. Maybe like the old lady in that book about rotten bananas."

This brief and cursory summary of *Pride's Way* might well have stumped even its own author in a game of charades, but I caught on immediately. I knew she was referring to the character in *Pride's Way* who didn't consider a banana ripe enough for human consumption until the skin was as black and stiff as an old shoe and the fruit flies were buzzing around. And who, when she went to visit her relatives, always carried along her own two-cup percolator.

At the time, this had sent my mother off into gales of laughter. Not because it struck her as being far-fetched, you understand, but because she had the same fierce and deep-rooted convictions about bananas and coffee pots. She had also, for the same reason and in the same spirit, hugely enjoyed Betty (*The Egg and I*) McDonald's description of her grandmother. That is, the one who always kept enough equipment in bed with her to start up light housekeeping. Although much more conservative, my mother always keeps several pocket book mysteries, her knitting, a flashlight, a box of Kleenex, a rosary, a box of wild cherry coughdrops, her folded nightgown, a jar of Vick's salve, and the latest *Cosmopolitan* under her pillow. The general effect is that of an Indian burial mound.

Yet even though my mother had heartily enjoyed these human interest touches, as depicted by *other* authors, she seemed strangely reluctant to give her own daughter a free hand. I say "strangely reluctant" because my mother, who will be seventy-nine as of next March, considers me the greatest living Catholic author of our time. Aside from this, her mind is still as clear as a bell.

"Mama," I now reminded her, "am I not the greatest living Catholic author of our time, bar none?"

"Certainly," she said in an unhappy voice. "It's just that I don't trust you, is all. You might unearth family secrets that should stay decently buried. Like the time"—and here her face flushed a deep crimson—"like the time I had my window washed for me."

Frankly speaking, my maternal ancestor and I do not always see eye to eye as to what constitutes a God-fearing standard of cleanliness. *I* clean house to restore a certain surface order; *she* cleans house to kill hidden microbes. As a matter of fact, she is probably the best hidden microbe killer in St. Joseph County, and she has no use for slatterns who fail to clean their bed springs every time they change the sheets.

Hence, I don't think she'll ever recover from the humiliation—the outrage, you might even say—inflicted upon her by an outspoken Hungarian neighbor who once lived next door to her. It was bad enough when this neighbor once cheated (in their Monday morning marathon to see who would get the wash hung out first) by doing her washing on a Sunday night and then sneaking it out at daybreak, but what broke my mother's spirit was *this.*

It seems that their kitchen windows were directly opposite each other and for about ten days, following a severe storm, my mother's kitchen window remained—let us face it!—very streaked and dirty. Her only excuse, and I consider it a mighty weak one, was that she had an injured sacroiliac at the time and didn't want to climb up on a stepladder. Anyhow, over marched the neighbor, bearing a pail of hot ammonia water, and—without so much as a by your leave—washed it for her. (The window, I mean. Not the sacroiliac.)

"My God, Mrs. Hardman!" she exploded. "I couldn't stand looking at that filthy window of yours another single day!"

The only episode in my mother's life that was possibly more humiliating, in her eyes, was the time the newsboy thought she had gone batty. It was Halloween and my two little girls wanted to go over and trick-or-treat their grandmother and scare her with their new costumes. So I called my mother up and said we'd be right over and, for heaven's sake,

to *act* scared when she opened the door. Instead, when the
doorbell rang, my mother decided to scare *them*. Crouching
way over so that her head was about three feet from the floor
and taking out her false teeth, she yanked open the door and
yelled "BOO YOURSELF!"

It was a terrible shock to the newsboy, a gangling youth
who hadn't yet achieved his full growth, and I'm not at all
sure he ever quite believed my mother's anguished explana‑
tion. After all, elderly ladies—living alone in big old houses
—*have* been known to lose their marbles. Anyway, my mother
says he was always very polite afterwards when he came
around for his collections but that he generally brought an‑
other boy along with him.

My mother, however, has a tendency to become embar‑
rassed too easily. Take, for example, the fact that—on the
night before she was married—she slept with the minister
who was to perform the ceremony. Few women can make this
claim; and yet this juicy little item, when we mention it before
strangers, always seems to embarrass my mother. After all,
as we carefully point out, wasn't the Reverend Grossnickle a
close friend of the family? Why the embarrassment? Maybe
it's because we don't always bother to explain that the Rev‑
erend Grossnickle was a woman, I wouldn't know.

(And now that I've had my fun, Mama insists that I repeat
in italics—for the benefit of any careless readers—that *the
minister was a woman*. And not only was she a close friend of
the family, but she had, before the wedding, been staying at
the house—helping with the trousseau sewing.)

Anyhow, the precise account of my mother's nuptials, as
set forth in the local *Tribune*, reads as follows: "Fairview
Chapel, Warren township, was the scene of a very pretty wed‑
ding on Sunday evening. After the close of the regular preach‑

ing services, and after the last hymn, Mrs. Alice Augustine began playing a wedding march. The doors were opened and Mr. H. Monroe Hardman led Miss Lottie Rennoe up the aisle to the pulpit where they were met by the pastor, Reverend Laura E. N. Grossnickle. In a few impressive words she pronounced them man and wife. The choir remained standing during the ceremony in honor of the groom, who is the church chorister. The young bride, who is a lady with rare qualities of heart and head, looked very sweet and pretty in tan colored henrietta with trimmings of silk and gimp. The happy young couple expect to make their home for the present with the groom's parents. *They have the earnest good wishes of every one of their many friends.*" (Italics mine.)

Another little item in the society columns reads thusly: "The Portage Cornet band met Wednesday evening of last week to do honor to their drum player, Mr. Monroe Hardman, who recently won for a bride Miss Lottie Rennoe. The band played an appropriate serenade and with the last strains came an invitation from the hospitable groom to enter the house, where they were served with fruit and other delicacies."

This, according to my mother, née Lottie Rennoe, is a rather glossed-over version as to what really took place. The band was invited into the house *not* after "the last strains" had died away but after someone, in a lively mood, fired a pistol into their darkened bedroom window, shattering not only the window but the kerosene lamp by the bed. It was *after* this that the hospitable groom arose and invited them into the house. The bride, who was annoyed by the pistol shot and all the broken glass, remained upstairs.

Now I feel that it is little everyday incidents like this, things that could happen to practically anyone, that give the necessary human interest touch to the personal essay. Only it took a lot of fancy talking before I finally swung my mother, despite her "rare qualities of heart and head," around to my way of thinking. Who, I asked her, would be interested in just reading items like the following: born in Canada into a family of nine children; christened Charlotte Mary Josephine by the parish priest; married at twenty; gave birth to five children; was widowed at the age of fifty-eight; returned to the Catholic fold two years later; was now financial secretary of the Bengalese Missionary Society and a member of the Altar and Rosary Society of Holy Cross Church? I wasn't (I said) writing an obituary notice.

What I intended to do, in a dignified way, was immortalize her in print just as Whistler had immortalized *his* mother on canvas. The only big difference would be that he, Mr. Whistler, had portrayed his mother with her hands folded in her lap. I could not see my way clear, I said, to portray my own mother in this unlikely position.

The truth of the matter is that my little white-haired mother is what I can only describe as an active menace to all the workingmen's unions in America, including the Hod Carrier's Local #18. That is, she's the sort of female who can splice electrical wires, fix dripping faucets and clogged drains, tighten chair springs, put down stair carpeting, replace windowpanes, insulate an attic, remove old wall paper, exterminate termites, plaster a ceiling, and lay linoleum. I am equally sure that she could, in an emergency, remove a man's appendix.

This is not to say, of course, that she doesn't have her daintier accomplishments. She is as skillful with a crochet hook and darning needle as with the more deadly instruments. All I'm saying is that her eyes positively gleam at the sight of a

ratchet screwdriver and her greatest joy in life is to wander
through hardware stores.

Recently her Altar and Rosary Society decreed that each
member should, for the greater glory of God and their de-
pleted treasury, earn a dollar by the sweat of her brow and
then report, at the next meeting, just what she'd done. Most
of the other ladies, of course, reported turning an honest dollar by baby sitting or selling crocheted pot holders or taking
Christmas card orders. *My* mother got up and reported that
she had taken her neighbor's sewing machine apart and oiled
it.

I do not, however, professionally loan my mother out to
the neighbors very often because there's enough repair and
maintenance work right on the premises to keep her happy.
Several years ago, for example, she did a very nice job of
painting the ceiling of our sun porch. And I could tell she was
terribly happy, up on her stepladder, because she always
whistles old Presbyterian hymns—like the *Doxology* or *Rock
of Ages* or *In the Garden*—when she is living life to the full.
Somehow, she has never seemed to master the swing of the
Catholic *O Salutaris*, catchy though it is, and perhaps it's just
as well. I mean, one associates the *O Salutaris* with the fra-
grance of incense rather than the cruder odor of turpentine or
lead paint or banana oil. The sentiment, however, remains the
same: a paean of praise to her Creator for having invented
such a delicious thing as manual labor.

Yet the cream of the jest, as far as I'm concerned, is that
my mother—with her small build, snowy white hair, and
gentle blue eyes—*looks* like a dear little old lady who
couldn't brew a cup of cambric tea. Just the other week the
dear little old lady, who gets fidgety if she doesn't have a
major project underway, decided to make me another needle-

point chair. After selling us the yarn and canvas, the saleslady carefully proceeded to explain the directions to my mother. "See, honey?" she said in a loud clear voice. "You start in the middle and work from right to left, one row at a time, and pull the yarn through like *this*." My mother smiled and nodded gratefully but the clerk later asked me, in an anxious aside: "Do you think she understood? Do you think she can manage?" I felt like saying that I thought she could not only manage the actual needlework but could, if she felt in the mood, carve a Louis XIV chair to go with it.

This misleading impression, this air of genteel and ladylike helplessness, is one of the greatest frauds of all times. Of all the women I know, I would nominate Charlotte Mary Josephine as the one most capable—that is, from the standpoint of ingenuity and fortitude—of taking care of herself on a South Sea desert island. Within twenty-four hours she would have a lean-to made of bamboo, a savory stew of wild herbs and pomegranates simmering over a trapper's fire, a blanket woven of rushes and sea weeds, and her long white underwear flying aloft—as an S.O.S. signal—from the tallest coconut tree.

But there I go—exaggerating to high heaven, as my mother would say—because I really doubt if she could shinny up a coconut tree at her age. Yet I don't need a desert island situation to show that my mother is not, and never has been, what you might call the helpless clinging vine type. For example, most women—three days after bearing a child—might be somewhat staggered at the thought of an unexpected and additional infant to handle, but not Charlotte Mary Josephine. Three days after I was born the neighbor across the street died in childbirth and left her frantic young husband with a brand new squalling infant named Vivian.

"Well," said my mother, as she shifted me over to one arm and made room for the squalling Vivian, "I hadn't counted on twins but I guess I can manage all right. Guess I can nurse two as well as one." Thus it is that my earliest photographs show me—not alone, in solitary splendor, on a bearskin rug —but alongside Vivian. Although there was scant resemblance between us, my mother enjoyed passing us off during that first year as bona fide twins. That is, she enjoyed it until the day when some woman, pointing to the blonde Vivian, said: "Well, that one is certainly the prettiest, isn't she?"

"Certainly *not*," snapped my mother, as she furiously wheeled the baby buggy on down the street. It is one of the few known instances when my mother refused to consider the evidence and then face up to reality.

I say that anyone who has the fortitude personally to select and buy her own tombstone, as my mother has insisted on doing, is *more* than facing up to reality. She has even, for that matter, given us explicit and cheerful directions as to how to arrange the corpse. "I want to be tilted to one side," she says, "instead of being laid flat on my back. I think it makes a corpse look so sort of helpless."

Along this same line, she has made elaborate arrangements for what she has been referring to, for the past twenty years, as My Last Illness. For the past twenty years, we (her children) have been trying to get her to wear the dainty nightgowns and bed jackets that we've given her for Christmas and birthday gifts. Folding them neatly away in her lower dresser drawer, she'll say: "Thanks so much, but I'll just save them for My Last Illness. No sense in wearing them now. I'll just pick up a few yards of plain outing flannel, at the January White Sales, and run up some everyday gowns in no time."

Three winters ago my mother fell down the cellar steps and

fractured her skull. When I, alone in the house, rushed to the
scene of the crash, I found her lying there in a pool of blood.
"Don't move!" I yelled. "I'll call the ambulance! Don't you
dare move!"

"Nonsense," said my mother. "If you won't help me to my
feet I'll get up by myself. I'm not going to any hospital wearing this housedress. I want to put on my navy blue crepe with
the polka dots."

The doctor later told me, while showing me the X-ray pictures, that it looked as if my mother had been hit over the
head with a hammer. My first impulse was to cry out, "I didn't
do it! I didn't do it!" because the horrible truth is that I was
tempted, at the time, to give her another clout. After all, I
had been instructed—back in my Camp Fire days—that it
was perfectly ethical to knock out a drowning person who re-
sisted aid. Yet, with one fracture already, I hesitated to hand
my mother another one.

I am still, to this day, wondering how a Red Cross worker
would have coped with my mother, but at the time I did my
bird-brain best. After helping her to her room and—with
trembling hands and many mental ejaculations—getting the
housedress over her bleeding head, I hit a new snag. My
mother decided that, along with the navy blue crepe, she also
wanted to change into her best *underskirt.* "Mama!" I yelled.
"This is an emergency!"

"All right, all right," she said, "you don't have to yell at
me. I won't bother to change my shoes but I'm *not* going one
step in this underskirt."

It was after this ordeal of getting my mother suitably ar-
rayed for her entrance into the hospital emergency room that
I decided that one should always—for stubborn cases like
this—keep a little chloroform on the pantry shelf. *That* would

settle my mother the next time she decided, at an awkward moment, to be one of the Ten Best Dressed Women in the country.

Anyway, my mother enjoyed her stay in the hospital immensely because she had a ringside bed in a big and crowded ward. She later refused to be moved into a private room, after once tasting the delights of the ward, because she couldn't bear to miss anything that was going on. It was practically as exciting as living in a police station, she reported happily, and ten times more comfortable.

Yet even her fractured skull was not a serious enough occasion to warrant, in her estimation, wearing one of the stored-away bed jackets. Those are for The Last Illness. Not just temporary periods of being somewhat indisposed.

As our family doctor says, with a pitying glance in my direction: "They just don't come like your mother any more. Nowadays, women just don't seem to have any staying power."

The only thing that I, the weakling daughter, can think of to build up my muscles and character is to take up fencing. My mother, who never throws anything away, recently handed me a July, 1897 copy of *Munsey's Magazine* wherein I perused an interesting article entitled "The Modern Swordswoman."

"Physicians appreciate and recommend fencing unreservedly," reads the article. "It quickens the pulse, stirs the blood, gives the muscles a moderate amount of work, and involves a minimum chance of injury, they say. The simple announcement that Mrs. J. Jacob Astor is one of the best fencers in New York has caused a perceptible increase in the demands for foils and fencing outfits."

Swayed by the influence of Mrs. J. Jacob Astor, I was on

the point of sending in for my foils when I came to the last
paragraph of the article. It stated baldly: "Undoubtedly,
fencing will add to woman's strength and poise but, with all
that, it cannot make a man of her."

I lost heart immediately.

Yet I really do feel that my mother has a better way to
"quicken the pulse and stir the blood" than did Mrs. J.
Jacob Astor in 1897. That is, my mother's perpetual zest
for acquiring new skills and in crossing off the list, one
by one, her secret little life ambitions. And whether her ambitions are your ambitions or Mrs. J. Jacob Astor's ambitions is
entirely beside the point.

Last summer Charlotte Mary Josephine fulfilled one of her
little dreams of glory while visiting on a farm in Southern
Indiana. They let her operate a tractor. She also, last summer,
got to tour the Brookfield Zoo in Chicago. It is true that she
took advantage of their wheelchair service but I feel that
wheelchairs are the only reasonable and civilized way to tour
zoos, anyway. Another fulfilled desire was to go up in a ferris
wheel. Another was to go down into Mammoth Cave in Ken-
tucky, wearing overalls, and take a rowboat ride on the sub-
terranean river.

My mother may, for all I know, be still seething with all
sorts of secret little desires but she has only expressed two.
She would like, for Mother's Day, to go into Clark's Restau-
rant ("Sea Foods Our Specialty") and order her first fresh
lobster: not for the gastronomical experience but because she's
just discovered it requires the skillful manipulation of a claw
cracker. She has never handled a claw cracker.

Her other expressed desire is a little more difficult to
understand. She would like, for some obscure reason, to stay
overnight—alone!—in a tourist cabin.

Her fresh lobster dream may very well be realized—for I am not an unreasonable person to live with—but as to the tourist cabin, NO. I flatly refuse to consider it, even though I would have no qualms about her welfare. I just feel that, if Charlotte Mary Josephine had nothing more to look forward to, she just might—one of these days—begin to grow old.

Mother Wins Her Wings

THERE'S SOMETHING about receiving a long distance call that always unnerves me. Even after I've made sure that no one has died or—equally important—that the charges aren't being reversed, I still am under a strain.

The whole trouble, I think, is that I've seen too many movies showing how busy tycoons handle *their* long distance calls. From behind a polished desk, with its barrage of ringing phones and a "Time Is Money" placard, the busy tycoon grabs up the phone that's been ringing the longest.

"R.F. speaking," he barks. "United Steel? Make it five thousand. Right!" and bangs down the receiver. Or, if it happens to be a social call, he barks: "R.F. speaking. Thursday? Sorry. I'll be in Bermuda. Make it Friday. Black tie? Right!" and bangs down the receiver. In any event, the tycoon always barks, is always cryptic, and always makes snap decisions. Time—is—money.

Bearing all this in mind, I always—whenever I get a long distance call—start out by barking. ("Susan! Turn down that radio! Janet! Find me a pencil! Louis! For heaven's sake, take Danny out in the kitchen and shut the door. *This is long distance!*")

This barking at my dear ones, however, is the best thing I do. I am not nearly so good at being cryptic or making snap decisions. That is, I'm cryptic enough but I occasionally find myself saying "Yes," very cryptically, to something I would not—under normal conditions—consider for one little minute.

A classic example of what I mean took place last May. I received a call from a Cleveland bookshop asking me if I couldn't, since I was coming to Cleveland anyway for a talk, arrive there in time for an afternoon autographing party. I replied that it was very sweet of them (which indeed it was, considering my book had already been out two years) but it would be physically impossible. The only train connection to Cleveland, I said, got me in around 6 P.M.

"Yes, we know," said the voice from Cleveland. "But we checked the airport and there's a 12:30 plane that would reach here around two o'clock. May we make the reservations for you?"

That would be terribly sweet of them, I said, but were they sure they *really* wanted me? After all, I said anxiously, it wasn't as if I had a new book to autograph. They *were* sure? Well, then, it certainly was kind of them and I'd be only too happy—et cetera, et cetera.

I hung up the receiver, feeling that I'd conducted myself with considerably more poise than usual, and called to my husband that he could come out from the kitchen. "Guess what?" I said, laughingly. "Some Cleveland bookshop wants to have an autographing party for me. Of course it's perfectly ridiculous, at this late date, but wasn't it sweet of them? They're even going to make the reservations at the airport for me. The book shop manager—I forget his name—is a Notre

Dame graduate who was in your brother Henry's class and
he . . ."

I stopped. My mind backed up. My stomach went cold.

Airport—reservations—what was I *saying*? This was some
ghastly mistake that was happening to someone else, not me.

Me, who had never been up in a plane and who had vowed
that nothing would ever *get* me up. Me, who couldn't even
bear to sit in a porch swing. Me, who couldn't even bear to
peer down from a double-decker bus. Me, who was as deathly
afraid of planes as other people were of the atomic bomb. Me,
who . . . "LOUIS!" I screamed. "I've got to *fly* to Cleveland.
Go up in an *airplane!*"

"Airplane?" echoed Danny. "Daddy, is Mama going up in
a real airplane? A four-motor passenger or a jet bomber?
Gee whiz, why does she get all the fun?"

The next two weeks, as I made my last-minute preparations
for what I considered my last days on earth, were packed with
fun. For one thing, I intended to leave no loose ends behind
me. I finished painting the white woodwork in the bedrooms
upstairs and also carefully packed away and labeled the children's winter coats and sweaters. (Poor little motherless
tykes! Who would be packing away their clothes *next* year?)
I also, in the evenings, got around to finishing Tolstoy's *War
and Peace:* a project I'd started back in 1935.

But my main project, during those two weeks, was to go
around buttonholing my friends and asking if *they* had ever
flown.

"Couldn't hire me," said some of them, gravely shaking
their heads.

"Yes," said others. "I went up *once*. Never again."

"Oh, I simply love it," said a few of the hardier ones. "It's

just like floating. Only be sure and sit in the front of the plane
instead of the back. It's smoother."

"Oh, no!" exclaimed the next person. "Sit in the back.
Then if there's a crash you at least have one chance in a thousand of crawling out. It's the front of the plane, you know, that
nosedives into the ground and bursts into flames."

"Look," I said to my husband. "Why don't I just cancel
those reservations and go by train? It would mean arriving
a day too early, but I'll bet Cleveland is an awfully interesting
city. I could visit the public library and the courthouse and
maybe take in a few museums . . ."

"Come, come," said my husband, who has never been up
in a plane, "there has to be a first time for everything. Besides,
think how this will strengthen your character."

I sent a brief note to Cleveland, confirming the time, and
added—for the benefit of the Welcoming Committee—a
thumbnail description of myself. "I will be the lady," I wrote,
"who gets off the plane with a green complexion, strong character lines in her face, and wearing a beige suit."

"Don't you think," said my next-door neighbor, who was
observing my daily decline, "that you're being awfully silly
about this? Why don't you just look at it this way? When
your number's up, your number's up. Besides, wouldn't you
rather have a sudden and violent death than a lingering last
illness in a T.B. sanitarium or a leper colony?"

What I really preferred, I thought to myself, was a death
from natural causes at the age of ninety-five in my own bed.
It was a tall order, all right, but if you were talking about
preferences. . . .

When I picked up the evening paper, the day before my
departure, it wasn't too difficult to read the handwriting on
the wall. There, in big black headlines, was the heartening

news that a United Airlines plane (which was to be *my* airline) coming from Cleveland (which was to be *my* destina-
tion) had crashed near Fort Wayne. Among the dead, stated
the local *Tribune*, were three South Bend women who were
up on their first flight.

"Now, look here," said my husband, "you have to be reasonable about this. It's a terrible tragedy, of course, but it
makes things better for you, mathematically speaking. By the
law of averages, there won't be another crash for simply ages."

"Sure," I said, "it just stands to reason." I got up and
walked out to the kitchen to check the liturgical calendar
hanging over the sink. Law of averages or no law of averages,
what I needed was some powerful heavenly intercession. Perhaps, I thought hopefully, I would be flying on some auspi-
cious feast day—under the patronage, say, of St. Christopher
or St. Jude. Dear Lord, I prayed, don't let tomorrow be just
a plain old ferial day.

It wasn't a ferial day. It was labeled "Vigil of the Feast
of the Ascension."

On the day of my ascension, my entire family—including
my mother—drove out to the airport to see me off. The sky
was as smooth and blue as a robin's egg but this, I felt gloom-
ily, didn't mean a thing. What did a blue sky have to do, for
example, with an engine conking out? Besides, the month of
May was a perfectly ducky month, here in the Midwest, for
sudden electrical storms. Like the storm that had caused the
Fort Wayne crash only two nights before.

Nor did it help my morale any when my husband took out
$10,000 worth of insurance on me at the airport. "It's just
routine procedure," he said, in a falsely hearty voice, but my
children—bless their little hearts—immediately brightened.
"Oh, Boy!" said Susan and Janet, in a sort of Anvil Chorus.

"You mean we'd really get $10,000 if the plane crashed? Oh, Boy!"

As I strapped myself into my seat, I felt that all that was lacking was the black hood, a priest in attendance, and a few reporters to jot down my last words. Once the motors had begun to roar, however, I decided that the electric chair, while not exactly cozy, had one big point in its favor. The condemned man could, as he walked the last mile, at least have a cigarette to soothe his nerves. *I* couldn't. The lighted sign over the pilot's door said I couldn't. All I could do was sit there, trapped like a rat, and listen for a possible knock in the roaring motors.

It was almost a relief when we started roaring down the runway. I shut my eyes, feeling the faster, faster, faster—so fast, indeed, that I couldn't even tell when we left the ground. Glory, I thought with relief, at this rate we'd be in Cleveland in perhaps another twenty minutes. Why, we were probably passing over Lake Erie right this minute.

The plane roared to a halt in midair. "Engine trouble," I said to myself. "Engine trouble over Lake Erie. I knew it, I *knew* it."

I wet my lips and leaned over to the man across the aisle. "Why have we stopped?" I said, in the barest of whispers. "What's the matter?"

He looked surprised. "Why, nothing's the matter," he said. "We're just turning around on the runway." He didn't add the word "Stupid!" but his look implied there ought to be a Federal law preventing females from boarding planes.

Again the roar of the motors—again, the faster, faster, faster—and then, with a little lurch of the plane, we left the good earth below us. When I finally scraped up the courage to peek out my window, I realized that the good earth was

very far below us. Only, every so often, we seemed to fall
down to meet it. And, when we weren't falling directly down,
we seemed to be tilting sidewise to meet it. Moreover, it was
impossible—considering the strangled sounds that were coming from the seat ahead of me—to pass it off as just *my* in-
flamed imagination. The man in front of me was retching
violently into his cardboard container.

I got out my container from under the seat but I reminded
myself, sternly, that it was all a matter of mental control. I
would just concentrate on pleasant memories from my past
life—like climbing the sand dunes at Lake Michigan, hunting
for shells, racing into the foamy waves, eating hot dogs and
potato salad. No, better not think of food—better not even
think of waves. . . .

What I really needed, I decided, as the plane dropped
another three feet, was a little human companionship. The
man in front of me was obviously in no condition for small
talk, but what about my friend across the aisle? Like the
Spartan he was, he was reading—or pretending to read—a
thick volume by Ford Madox Ford. There was something
about him . . . his literary taste? his noble brow? his scholarly
detachment? . . . that seemed oddly familiar. As a faculty
wife, I could—so to speak—almost *smell* his profession.

"Pardon me," I said, leaning across the aisle, "but are you,
by any chance, an English professor?"

Putting his finger in Ford Madox Ford, to keep the place,
he closed the book and stared somberly ahead of him. Finally
he spoke. "I am in labor," he said sternly.

For a startled half-second, I thought of ringing for the
stewardess (heavenly days, he was in even worse shape than
the man in front of me!) and then I remembered, with relief,
that there was also such a thing as Labor, capital L. I racked

my brains trying to think of something really intelligent to say about Labor (I just *couldn't* let this budding conversation die) and then leaned across the aisle.

"And have you," I asked brightly, "read the Pope's Encyclicals on Labor?"

"I have," he said sternly, and picked up Ford Madox Ford. *Ite, conversation est. . . .*

Ten minutes later, the Man in Labor leaned across to me. "But I used to be an English professor," he admitted, "at the University of Wisconsin."

I smiled and leaned back in my seat, my faith in my smelling powers justified. Only, were all men in Labor so cautious and guarded in their statements? Who did he think I was, anyway? A stool pigeon for Senator McCarthy? At the rate he was unbending, it would take a trans-Atlantic flight, perish the thought, even to get his literary views on Ford Madox Ford . . .

The plane dropped another three feet.

"Your attention, please," said the airline hostess. She was standing in front of the pilot's door, waiting for our undivided attention. Was she, I wondered, going to read a few prayers? Lead us in a little community singing? *Anything*, I thought, would be welcome. *Anything* to make me forget I was swaying and falling through space; that my ear drums were about to explode like Chinese firecrackers; that my stomach. . . .

"We seem," announced the stewardess, in what I considered the understatement of the year, "to be having a rather rough flight. The pilot is trying to climb higher. Perhaps it will be smoother at a higher altitude. However, we ask that you keep your safety belts adjusted for the remainder of the flight. Thank you."

Then she leaned over to the passenger in the front seat and

whispered something to him. He shook his head in a violent
negative. Then she moved on to the next passenger and whispered in *his* ear. His hand flew to his mouth, in instinctive
recoil.

What in the world was she whispering about? What dread
proposal was she putting up to us? Were we to take our choice
of staying with the ship or jumping with parachutes?

I braced myself as she turned toward me. Dear Lord, I
prayed, help me to make the right decision. Let me be a credit
to my family, my country, my Church. . . .

"Would you," whispered the stewardess, "feel like some
lunch? We're serving cold sliced turkey, glazed sweet potatoes, Waldorf salad, and strawberry shortcake. Would you
care for a tray?"

"Why, yes, I believe I will," I heard myself saying, as if
under a spinal anesthesia. The stewardess gave me a little
incredulous smile and hurried away. In a few minutes she
was back with a little pillow. Did she, I wondered, think I was
delirious? She put the pillow in my lap, oddly enough, and
then scurried away again.

When she came back with the loaded tray, placing it *on* the
pillow, I thought I detected a new attitude in her. Her first
incredulity seemed to have given way to awe. She even smiled
at me as if she were rather proud of me. Not so my other
shipmates.

As I speared a piece of cold turkey, the Man in Labor shot
me a look of positive dislike. Feeling that our friendship,
which had been fragile at best, was gone forever, I decided I
had nothing more to lose. Pointing to the tray, I shouted
"GOOD!" with my mouth half full, and was rewarded with a
look that defies description. The closest I could come to it

would be "Grosse bête!" in French or "Ugh!" in the Red Man's language.

Just as I was spooning up the last drop of strawberry short-cake, the hostess announced: "Your attention, please. We will be landing at the Cleveland airport in a few minutes. We hope you have enjoyed your flight. Thank you."

There was barely enough time to take a last swig of coffee and wipe the strawberry juice off my chin, but I couldn't help feeling it was very nice timing. I wasn't *too* sure, despite my vulgar showing off, just how long the lunch would stay with me.

"And how," asked the one-woman Welcoming Committee at the airport, "did you enjoy your first flight?" (She recognized me right off, I guess by the strong character lines in my face.)

"Oh, it was pretty rough," I said, with all the relish of a person describing how many blood transfusions he'd needed, "but I weathered it better than the others. Do you know that I was the *only* one who ordered any lunch? I guess," I added in belated humility, "that I was so scared that my stomach was just *numb*."

The Welcoming Committee looked sympathetic. "But now that you've been up," she said, "I'll bet you'll enjoy your return flight."

I was already walking toward the airport office. "Oh, I'm cancelling *that*," I said. "I'm going back on the New York Central."

After all, I'd won my wings. Just how much character did people expect of me, anyway?

House of Light

A"WHY I BECAME" conversion story is generally the first
project on a convert's agenda but I, in my writing, have
always skated neatly around the subject. It was *my* story:
personal to a degree, important only to myself, and almost
embarrassing in its simplicity. Alongside the soul-wrestling,
truth-ferreting, pillar-to-post epics of other converts, it would
sound like *Little Red Riding Hood* compared to *The Brothers
Karamazov*.

Yet this is not to imply, heaven forbid, that I didn't *like*
my own story. To me, it was a fascinating demonstration of
the inscrutable ways of God—suddenly thrusting the gift of
faith into the surprised hands of a most unlikely candidate. It
was just that I saw no need, nor did I have the heart, to expose
my own witless role in the whole proceedings.

In now doing so, I can only hope that my non-intellectual
approach to the Church will have, if nothing else, a certain air
of novelty about it.

In other words, I am outside the pale of that intellectually
respectable league of converts who can say, "It was Augustine
who led the way," or "Aristotle left me strangely dissatisfied,"

or "The scales fell from my eyes when I first read the *Summa* in the original," or "After twenty years as a Communist I one day chanced to read the Pope's Encyclical on Labor."

My sole intellectual approach to the Church consisted in lifting my index finger and pushing the buzzer at a Catholic rectory. True, I wasn't trying to sell Fuller brushes but I can't say that I had anything much heavier on my mind. I pushed that buzzer guided by little more than my woman's intuition that here, perhaps, was the place to fulfill my part of a childish bargain.

Thus, in a very literal sense, I can say in the words of Léon Bloy: "For my part, I declare that I never sought or found anything unless one wishes to describe as a discovery the fact of tripping blindly over a threshold and being thrown flat on one's stomach into the House of Light."

Six weeks after falling flat on my stomach, I—a twenty-one year old Presbyterian—was baptized a Catholic. In retrospect, I would be tempted to say—if it were not for my profound respect for the doctrine of Divine Providence—that it was all a matter of sheer fool's luck and nothing else.

All convert stories, in the telling, seem to fall into two sharp divisions: the "man pursues God" versus the "God pursues man" plot. Yet something tells me that all converts— even the most "self-made" ones—will, in the lucid light of eternity, see their little plots as a clear-cut case of God pursuing them.

I am perfectly aware that this is an attitude that frequently irritates, even scandalizes, the more "humble" citizens. "You mean," they say, "that God was paying all that attention to *you?*" To which, as far as I can figure out, there is only one truly humble answer: "Yes." And I think that this open-faced acknowledgment—with its "You have not chosen Me, I have

chosen you" implication—is one of the most stirring aspects
of conversion.

I bring this up for the benefit of brand-new converts or
those outsiders who are making a first tentative move toward
the Church. I think they sense this drawing power—this
thrilling and personal feeling that God has, so to speak, put
his finger on them—but are almost afraid to think it out loud.
Presumption! Enough to make the high priests rend their
garments! Yet, how they'd like to believe it.

To those timid souls I say: "Go on. Believe it." Not only
is it the truth, based on straight doctrine, but it begets a deeper
gratitude, and a deeper gratitude, in turn, begets a deeper
love of God. All of which reminds me of a permanent feature
in my diocesan newspaper: the picture of a smiling Christ,
at the tender age of around three, pointing his finger at you
and saying:

"You—I seek
You—I mean
You—Yes, You—I love you."

It's really somewhat corny, what with the infant Christ resembling Shirley Temple in her heyday, but the underlying
truth of the sentiment expressed . . . ah, you can't fight that.

Therefore, when I say that I—entirely under my own steam
—pushed that rectory buzzer, don't get me wrong. I have no
illusions whatsoever, despite my splendid steam, that I engi-
neered the whole project by myself. All I really did, as will
be explained later, was to keep my part of a bargain.

There is also the possibility that Catholicism, like a hidden
virus, was already in my blood stream. As I later discovered,
I should have been a Catholic all along. My mother had been
baptized a Catholic but her heritage, while she was still a

small child, and through no fault of her own, had also been
lost by the wayside. Then along came her marriage to a
staunch Presbyterian who couldn't abide Catholics, and that
was that.

With my father a Presbyterian deacon and my mother a
"fallen-away" Catholic, my three brothers and I automatically became little Presbyterians. Very bored and automatic
ones, too. God (a vague character, He) belonged strictly in
Sunday School, and Sunday School, with just its Moses in
the bullrushes stories, was pretty deadly. Any resemblance
between those stories and a personal and vital religion was
purely coincidental.

I cannot claim to have closely examined, in my youth, the
Presbyterian tenets of belief and found them wanting. But, if
I *had* wanted to examine them, I'm sure it would have taken
considerable research first to find them. For instance, the only
"doctrinal quiz"—in order to graduate into the Intermediate
Department—was to memorize St. Paul's "Now I see as
through a glass darkly" epistle to the Corinthians. Nothing
could have been more appropriate.

In the Senior Department, my glass grew even darker. I
remember, in particular, how darkly irritating were the
"Thought For The Week" bulletins that were posted in the
front churchyard. The most irritating one was "God Is Love."

I remember thinking they had the verb wrong. Did they
mean "God loves us" or "God is lovable" or "God wants
love" or "God represents love" or just what? Certainly, "God
Is Love" was a senseless tidbit to throw at a person.

Since becoming a Catholic, I have discovered (especially
through Thomas Merton) that when St. John said "God Is
Love," he uttered one of the most bona fide, most metaphysical, most "heart of the matter" statements in all theology. But

my Presbyterian teachers never attempted (and with very good reason probably) to explain it. God, *in Himself,* was never discussed. Perhaps they felt that St. Paul, with his dark mirror, meant you shouldn't even try to investigate God? By way of proof positive that doctrinal teaching wasn't considered too important, I want you to know that even *I* was asked to teach Sunday School. Would you want someone who can barely count to ten on his fingers to teach your child mathematics?

It is more than possible, of course, that I was an extremely religion-resistant child, but the point remains that I scorned every inch of that church—not from an intellectual point of view but just from sheer boredom. I can still see the big gilt organ pipes and the minister's platform with its wooden pulpit, flanked by the American flag at one end and a potted palm at the other. Empty, empty boredom.

Stage properties, naturally, have nothing to do with religion, per se, but I have since been in incredibly ugly and garish Catholic churches (outraging every possible tenet of good taste) and *still* found what was needed—a sense of prayer and a sense of mystery. One need not even know about the Blessed Sacrament to catch the general idea that here is a place to kneel, not just sit and be talked to.

Or prayed at. Prayer in my Presbyterian church consisted in slightly lowering your chin while the minister, raising his chin, did your praying for you. With everything depending on the one-man performance of the minister, there was never so much as three minutes' quiet during the entire services to "freewheel" on your own. And yet they talk about that personal and direct Protestant approach to God!

May all good Protestant readers forgive me my vehemence. I come to bring peace, not the sword—when it comes to re-

*ligious tolerance—but this happens to be a personal report.
It is by no means a blanket indictment. It's just a personal
recording of what I happened to find in my own particular
Presbyterian church. Or, rather, didn't find.*

When I went off to Milwaukee-Downer College ("An insti-
tution of higher learning for cultured and refined young
ladies"), I was happy indeed to leave my "religion" behind
me. But what did I find awaiting me? Not only daily non-
sectarian chapel—with the same pulpit, American flag, and
potted palm—but the ruling that we had to attend some Milwaukee church every Sunday. It wasn't even done on the
honor system; there were monitors to flush you out of your
room at 10:30. So, to relieve the tedium, I went—with a
beautiful impartiality—to a different Protestant church each
week and, when I had run the gamut, I quit.

Thereafter I cheated. When it came time for church I hid
in my clothes closet, sitting cross-legged on the floor, and
spent the time reading by flashlight. I preferred sitting there,
amid laundry bags and tennis shoes and with my dresses batting me around the ears, to attending a church of any kind.
("I fled Him, down the nights and down the days . . .")

Two years later I switched to the University of Wisconsin,
the so-called "Playground of the Middle West." Here, certainly, there was no need to hide in closets. All the while I was
at the University of Wisconsin, I darkened no church door
and, naturally, wouldn't have been caught dead saying any
private prayers. Now, at long last, I was "free." Life, for me,
came to mean only clothes, dancing, men, and how many prom
bids and fraternity pins one could collect in a season. As far
as anything spiritual went, I was just waltzing along: not
searching, not interested, not even aware that anything was
missing.

There was just one little thing at Wisconsin that might have indicated that the Hound of Heaven was closing in on me. In my Gamma Phi Beta sorority there were only a few Catholics and I, Lucile, had to draw one for a roommate. A McCarthy, even. I had to draw a McCarthy.

When I discovered, in quick order, that I had drawn not only a Catholic but a naïve little Bernadette, I felt that I was putting up with a great deal. Perhaps we would be in the thick of one of those bull sessions (What is the meaning of Life-Sex-Art?) out on the smoking porch. Suddenly, I would look around. Where was the roommate? It would irk me that she would slip quietly away, sincerely not interested in our final judicious verdicts. She would also slip quietly away in the middle of a risqué story.

Then, too, she embarrassed me not only by actually kneeling down to say her night prayers, glass rosary in hand, but by going about it as earnestly as if she were calling God, or one of his saints, on the telephone. She never paraded or explained her religion (and I let well enough alone) but every once in awhile she'd say things—weird little things. If I were upset over something she'd say casually, "Don't worry. I offered up my Communion for you this morning." Or, "I'll remember to ask the Little Flower to help you out." I never said much more than "Ummm" to any of this and she never expected more. But (believe me!) I would have said more than "Ummm" if she had ever said outright: "I am praying for your soul." Perhaps the most enraging remark in the entire English language.

The *pièce de résistance*, however, was the way she—a bright, pretty, popular, and apparently normal girl—would get up in the morning and tiptoe off to Mass, rain or shine or hailstorm. Sunday was all right—Catholics were forced to go

on Sundays—but this was during the week, for Pete's sake. It
certainly took all kinds to make a world . . .

Yet it was odd the way I began to regard one of my English
instructors with growing distaste. His was a class in Renais-
sance Satire, and he was an excellent teacher, but some of
those little classics of Erasmus and Rabelais were crawling
with innuendoes, to put it mildly, against my roommate's religion.

Well, no one loves a vicious satire more than I but, for some
odd reason, I began to feel a little huffy and defensive. I felt
defensive on behalf of defenseless McCarthy in much the same
way as I would blindly defend an underdog. And McCarthy
was an underdog because she was saddled, from birth, with
a religion that could only mean a hard life for a female.

Poor McCarthy! Never any reasonable divorce, never any
reasonable birth control. I could only picture the worst: Poor
McCarthy chained for life to some drunken brute who beat
her every Saturday night; drearily bearing an unwanted child
every year because the Church, like a monster, demanded it.

Since this caricature was the sum total of my knowledge of
Catholicism, small wonder I felt sorry for McCarthy. (Who,
in case anyone is interested, now lives in Evanston, Ill.; is the
proud and happy mother of five children; and whose "drunken
brute" of a husband is one of my favorite men.) Yet at the
same time, as I was saying, I began to resent that professor's
witty and mocking remarks in class. Catholicism might be a
hard and backward religion, and strictly for peasants, but it
didn't strike me as one to be treated as a joke. Something also
told me that Erasmus and Rabelais were not presenting the
whole of Catholicism. I could see for myself that my roommate seemed to be living another version.

Finally, one day, I let loose on a term paper. I did a good

job of abusing the Church (later receiving an A for my efforts) and then, at the bottom of the paper, I wrote belligerently: "Okay. Here's your paper. But some day *I'm* going to be one of these Catholics."

Why I wrote that, I wouldn't know. Naturally, I intended no such thing. Perhaps I just wanted to show "Laughing Boy" that I wasn't swallowing everything, hook, line, and sinker. But me be a Catholic? I should even *investigate* a religion that might trap me into a dog's life such as faced McCarthy? Ho!

I was completely happy, having a wonderful time on the shores of Lake Mendota, wearing a Protestant's fraternity pin, and God (that vague character, He) was the least of my worries. One's broken-down old age was time a-plenty for looking into the "life is real and life is earnest" stuff.

Nevertheless, just four months after writing that thoughtless and belligerent threat on my term paper, I was baptized a Catholic. This, I feel, calls for a little explanation.

In my last semester I suddenly became mysteriously ill and was sent home from college. Not only was I alarmed and frightened by the illness but upset at the possibility of not getting back with my graduating class. The doctors only shrugged their shoulders as I entered the clinic for treatments and so, alone and frightened, I had but one alternative. I wrote McCarthy not only to send home my trunk but to send up some of her prayers.

I also decided to pray for myself (what did I have to lose?) but I found out it wasn't so easy. God had, by now, become a mere will-o'-the-wisp and I felt very awkward and foolish and *alone* in my approach. I wavered uneasily between the notion that there must be *some* sort of God and the feeling that I was addressing thin air.

Moreover, I had just enough Emily Post in me to be socially

embarrassed about the "give me" situation. How have the
nerve to beg help from someone you'd never paid any attention
to? Someone, in fact, who had bored you to distraction all
your life? All in all, I felt somewhat like Emily Dickinson
when she wrote:

> Of course I prayed—
> And did God care?
> He cared as much as
> On the air
> A bird had stamped her foot
> And cried "Give me!"

So, to save face, I struck a bargain. "God," said I, "who-
ever and wherever you are, if you'll deliver me from this unknown plague I promise, on my word of honor, to investigate
you."

Thank God, I kept that promise. By April I was cured and,
as soon as the last bandages were removed, I hied myself to a
priest. Not only had I never talked to one before, but I still
don't know why I thought a Roman Catholic priest was the
logical person to explain God to me. Certainly, my Renais-
sance Satire class hadn't extolled the Roman clergy!

Moreover, I still wasn't particularly interested in God or
too profoundly grateful for my recovery. (That is, how did I
know if God had really had a hand in it?) I was just uneasily
keeping my part of a solemn bargain. *Noblesse oblige!* Big-
hearted me, giving God a break.

But! One session with that priest and God became the most
exciting and absorbing topic in the world. My attitude was not
so much "Prove God exists, priest!" as "Can you make God
seem real, priest?"

He could. Not in the sense that he reduced God's mystery

but that he increased my conception of the staggering "Before
Abraham was, I am" reality of the mystery. There was, I
found, a vast difference between "fuzziness" and "mystery."

Naturally, I had no penetrating theological questions on
tap to disconcert and floor that priest. I couldn't even think
(my mind was so barren) of any particular problems I wanted
solved. So Mother Church, ever solicitous, *presented* me with
problems. One of the first questions in the Catechism was a
honey: "Why was I born?"

After letting me flounder around for awhile ("To do good?
To develop one's personality? To seek beauty, whatever that
might be?") the Church gave me the answer in one sentence:
"To know God, to love Him, to serve Him in this world, and
be happy with Him forever in the next." Then the Church, ever
solicitous, started turning on the floodlights . . .

Never was there any apology or hedging or compromising
behind those floodlights. There was no "It is generally conceded" or "We feel perhaps that this doctrine is the more
reasonable of the two" preamble to anything. The Church
was positive it had the right answers and the divine right to
guard those right answers.

After so many years, it is difficult to remember just what
it was in Catholic apologetics—that firm, logical, relentless,
brick-upon-brick, apologetical "stacking up"—that impressed
me most. One doesn't stand at the foot of Pike's Peak and say:
"Ah, isn't that sixth crag from the top impressive?" For me,
it was the impressive whole.

What I most vividly remember is that, after only a few
sessions, I was positive I wanted (not was going) to become a
Catholic. I wanted to become a Catholic so badly that I was
frightened lest—any minute!—I was going to hit a doctrine
I couldn't possibly accept.

When we arrived at the doctrine of Transubstantiation (a $5 word meaning "change of one entire substance into another" and referring to the Holy Eucharist), a cold chill ran down my spine. This was it! This finished me off! I arose from that session—very quiet, very subdued—and went home and read, as per instruction, the sixth chapter of St. John over again. After several readings I could only agree with the Jews that it was a hard saying, and I didn't blame them for turning away. I, too, must turn sadly away but, still, I would go back for one more session . . . politely to turn in my sweat shirt.

In that session the priest happened to take me into the Log Chapel at Notre Dame. (I'd lived in South Bend all my life but had never been anywhere on the campus but the football stadium.) Anyway, the priest was giving me the tourist's tour —pointing out the burial place of the first priest ordained in the United States, the Indian murals on the walls, the ancient altars—when I, only half-listening to him, burst out with what was really on my mind. It was that old time-honored Protestant question: "If Catholics *really* believe that God is really and truly present on their altars, why don't they crawl into church on their hands and knees?"

And suddenly I knew, with a shock, that what I was really thinking was: "Why aren't we on our hands and knees right this minute instead of standing here like tourists?"

It is impossible for me to explain this sudden turn-about-face. All I know is that the Blessed Sacrament, over the years, has been one of the strongest points in my faith.

After the Transubstantiation crisis, I felt only a great urgency to be baptized immediately. Let me pick up the loose ends later! Baptism by desire and baptism by blood were all very well, but as for me on my Sahara desert—water! lots of water! and fast!

One might well think that the swiftness and impulsiveness of my conversion boded no good. This could never last. All I can say, lamely, is, "Well, but it did." Moreover, I resent those people who always quote: "First fervor is false fervor." If that be an infallible rule, then practically all of the New Testament conversions were mighty shallow affairs. Too, those New Testament conversions were very speedy affairs. Christ's apologetics was often just two words: "Follow me," and his listeners fell over their own feet to do so.

But back to my own story. That June, instead of receiving my diploma as an art student, I received the seven gifts of the Holy Ghost. Who is to say I didn't get the best of the bargain? Moreover, one year later my mother took instructions and, after forty-seven years, returned to the fold. One year later I met and married a very solid born Catholic: Louis Hasley, an English instructor at Notre Dame.

Two children arrived in quick succession, and the following years were more involved with pursuing them than in pursuing higher theology. All went smoothly as far as the Catholicism was concerned, with nary a doubt or a problem on the horizon. As I now look back, it was just *too* smooth. I now refer to this period as "The Great Lull."

I had enough Catholicism to operate on but not enough to "grow on." The straight apologetics was now fairly well under control (I'd belonged to a Catholic study group for six years), but apologetics, as I now see it, is only a necessary prelude. After digging the cellar you should go ahead and build your spiritual house.

Eight years ago, into this Great Lull, there suddenly came another of those neatly camouflaged blessings. I suddenly found myself flat on my back with a heart condition that the specialists cheerfully assured me was permanent. From now on I would be a heart cripple and a semi-invalid.

There is nothing, I maintain, like staring at the ceiling for four weary months, thinking that Life has ended up a blind alley, to make one's disposition become either very "Thy will be done"-ish or rebellious. I was the rebellious sort. This was a fine trick for God to play on a friend who was just minding her own business and not hurting anyone.

I now concede it *was* a fine trick. For it was lying there in bed, reading anything and everything I could get my hands on, that I stumbled across a veritable gold mine—good Catholic writing. Péguy, Bernanos, Mauriac, Bloy, Sigrid Undset, Chesterton, Houselander, Greene, and others. These gifted writers could, in one flashing metaphor, illuminate certain truths that many of the theologians and philosophers—with their dry and measured approach—simply deadened for me.

Even more important, from my standpoint, were the saint-writers who could tell you how to build spiritual houses: St. Teresa of Avila, Francis de Sales, St. John of the Cross, Elizabeth of the Trinity, Catherine of Sienna. Doors started opening on doors . . .

At this point the practical reader may ask: "With a born Catholic husband, teaching English in a big Catholic university, why this belated discovery of the Catholic classics?"

I, too, ask "Why?" For years I had been dusting some of those very books I was now so enraptured over. Why hadn't my husband told me to quit my infernal dusting and read them? Why hadn't the priest who converted me left me with a spiritual reading list? Why hadn't *anyone* told me these things?

Lying in bed, I began to get a little bit mad at all born Catholics. A selfish, selfish crew. Finally I could contain myself no longer and, calling for pencil and pad, I furiously composed my first Catholic essay. If no one would share the hidden wealth with converts, *I* would look after them.

Frankly, that first essay of mine would have made the scholarly Newman turn over in his grave. It was very much like writing a travel book on Mexico, after spending a weekend just over the Rio Grande border.

When I showed it to the priest who came over to the house to bring me Holy Communion, he practically collapsed with uncouth mirth. "No Catholic editor in his right mind would print this," he said, "but—well, you might try. It's—uh—rather refreshing."

Lo! To my great amazement, this housewife (having easily found an editor of unsound mind) suddenly found herself a so-called Catholic writer overnight. Personal essays started sliding off my bedspread with an alarming rapidity and no one, to date, has managed to stem the tide.

But let us not leave me in bed. After four months of this feverish one-man Catholic revival (hardly recommended for heart ailments), I arose from my pallet and went to the Ann Arbor Clinic to see how many more months I had left to live.

Although I was so weak I could hardly walk, I gathered from their reports that they had seldom seen a finer specimen of rugged American womanhood. My heart was not only in splendid condition—splendid!—but they didn't think anything had been wrong in the first place.

My first reaction was nothing short of murderous. Sticking a busy housewife and mother in bed for four months for no good reason! My second reaction, as the blood receded from my brain, was a little more mellow. That session in bed had amounted to a "second conversion" and, like missing my diploma years before, I had come out ahead in the bargain. I had discovered, among other things, the existence of ascetical and mystical theology: meaning that precise, well-documented, well-illustrated study of the spiritual life. Why was I born?

The saints thought it was in order to start becoming saints and were only too eager to point the way.

I had, in particular, discovered gentle Francis de Sales, and de Sales had urged: "If thou wouldst walk in earnest toward devotion, seek some good man to conduct and guide thee." That is, a personal spiritual director.

I'd never heard of such a thing before but it seemed like a sound idea, this getting more personal direction than is possible in the Saturday afternoon confessional, and I—for one —could *use* direction. For, since you can't see yourself as you really are, why not ask a professional to take a look? The result might be (and in truth proved to be) quite startling: like turning a flashlight on a dark cobwebby corner and watching the spiders run for cover. Self-love, pride, impatience, spiritual gluttony, intolerance. . . .

But, if I thought that a spiritual director would immediately put me on a very interesting monastic schedule of some sort and that I would become lean, holy, and ascetical in three easy lessons, I had another think a-coming. My monastic schedule —with the exception of frequent weekday Mass and Communion, *if* it didn't interfere—proved to be a firm turning back to the kitchen sink. State of life! Just as before! Except, as I learned, with just this one difference: approaching that state of life with a new Catholic awareness and set of values, thus shifting gears from the purely natural to the supernatural.

So much for the home front. Then, one day, I chanced to hear Ann Harrigan—who was then director of Chicago Friendship House—give a talk on the Mystical Body, with special reference to race prejudice. Once again I found myself profoundly jarred. I was now busily polishing my own little soul (or, rather, starting to sand off the sharper edges) but not paying much attention to anyone else. Was I, as a Catholic, being the salt of the earth, my brother's keeper, a Christ-bearer into the marketplace? Not so you could notice.

This first introduction to the lay apostolate, along with my subsequent close friendship and work with Ann Harrigan, proved another turn in the road. I was now—at long last!—getting God, self, and neighbor into the proper Catholic focus, but new converts to the Church today needn't take as long as I did to do it. During the past decade, there has been a great stirring of the waters; a new awareness, along all fronts, of the urgent need to restore all things in Christ. It is not the time for an ivory tower Catholicism or any retreating into the desert. Catholics are called to spread Christ's fire upon the earth, not just hug their wonderful gift of faith to themselves.

Only in a very limited sense can one say at Baptism: "Here's the finale. Peace, it's wonderful." The Church offers peace, yes, but if it's just a rocking-chair sort of peace you're after, I would recommend some nice quiet sanitarium in the hills of New Hampshire rather than the Roman Catholic Church.

Baptism is only the beginning, the orchestra tuning up, the curtain rising on the most important and absorbing drama in the world: man's relationship with God. As Chesterton says: "Have you ever known what it is to walk along a road in such a frame of mind that you thought you might meet God at any turn of the path?" For this, a man must have a perpetual receptiveness. Not just a "Peace, it's wonderful" placidity.

It is precisely this wonderful, endless exploration along the right road, with its interesting detours and unexpected vistas, that I—personally—would hold out to people interested in Catholicism. "Peace" is perhaps the last word to spring to my mind. I can think only in terms of the adventure, the aliveness, the challenge, the diversity, and—yes!—the joyousness of the Catholic way of life.

The Written Word

THE ELABORATE communication system we have in our home might well lead a stranger to believe that the Hasleys were not on speaking terms; were a family of deaf-mutes; or were all given to frequent attacks of laryngitis. None of these suppositions, however fascinating, would be true. We leave notes for each other and pin up placards and post bulletins because—without the written word staring us in the face—our whole way of life would collapse.

For instance, the daily bulletin posted in the bathroom is of vital importance. Without it, what with five people with one bathroom to share between them, we would start the day with a hopeless traffic snarl on our hands. Hence, the bulletin may go something like this: "Susan, wake Janet. Janet, wake Daddy. Daddy, wake Mother and Danny." Or, if Daddy doesn't happen to have an eight o'clock class at Notre Dame, it may read: "Susan, wake Janet. Janet, wake Mother but not Daddy. Mother, wake Daddy in time for Mass." My favorite version of this rise-and-shine schedule, of course, ends up with: "Be very quiet. Let Mother sleep. Up very late last night."

In any event, Susan is always the trigger man because her

toilette, for some mysterious reason, always takes the longest.
I say it's mysterious because, after all, she does not—as does
Janet—have to go through the daily agony of deciding which
sweater looks best with which skirt or which charm bracelet
and scarf go best with the final ensemble. St. Mary's Acad-
emy, which requires a uniform, leaves our trigger man with
the simple choice of wearing a green wool suit or a green
wool suit. Offhand, this would seem a relatively easy decision to face—even for early morning—and yet *la toilette de
Susan* holds up the bathroom for a good thirty minutes.
(Which reminds me of the man trying to comfort the father
of the bride: "Think of it this way, chum. You're not losing
a daughter—you're just gaining a bathroom.") Anyhow, I
feel that it is only fitting that Susan be made to pay her debt
to society. That is, being the first one to be routed out of bed.

Next in importance to the *chambre de bath* bulletin, I would
say, are the various communiqués in the refrigerator. An egg
may have printed on its shell: "I am hard-boiled. For Susan's
lunch." Another sign, on top of a glass of milk, may read
accusingly: "Janet! You didn't finish this." A dab of left-over
gravy, and my mother is very fond of preserving dabs, may
bear the suggestion: "Use in hash?" The most frequent sign,
naturally, to appear on anything edible is: "Hands off. This
means YOU."

On the kitchen work table one comes across further communications of either a restraining or a bullying nature. Such
as a fluttering sign attached to a box of raised doughnuts: "The
limit is one, after school. No eating after 4:30." Or a week-day
note pinned to some cellophane-wrapped delicacy, like a
Banana Twinkie, may read: "Janet, if you're going to communion, take this. If eating at home, eat toast." Or, on cold

winter mornings, this official command to the first person who gets downstairs: "Bring in milk."

The grocery list over the kitchen sink enables everyone—via the written word—to cite his own particular gastronomical likes or dislikes. Such as: "Bread. No caraway seeds, please." —"Get some *good* cookies for a change. Not always fig newtons."—"Breakfast cereal—Danny wants the box with a cutout mask on it."—"Liver sausage. Don't let them slice it—gets too messy."

The kitchen calendar was originally intended to mark the passing of the seasons, and also serve as a liturgical guide, but the cockle of the written word has long since crept in among the wheat. There are penciled citations reminding one of dental appointments, haircuts, volleyball games, apostolic gatherings, deadlines for editors, birthday parties, P.T.A. meetings, faculty lectures, ballet lessons, and parish bazaars —along with more mundane reminders to soften the water, order fuel oil, collect stuff for a rummage sale, and turn in the raffle tickets for the Altar and Rosary Society.

Yet even if one cannot, under all this scribbling, distinguish a double-ranking first class feast from a ferial day, a little of the liturgical message still shines through. That is, you can still see the little red fish for Friday, gleaming through the network of penciling, and also—unless it's been a *very* busy month—the liturgical message at the top of the calendar. (March. "The feast of St. Isidore, the Farmer, has been inserted into the Church Calendar for America on the 22nd of this month. He was a poor working man," et cetera, et cetera.)

Regretfully leaving the kitchen and its quaint customs behind us, as Fitzpatrick would say in his travelogue movies, let us travel on to the living room. Here we find that the living room desk is regarded by the natives as the proper place for all telephone communications: "Mother, some man called. Sounded like a priest. Call this number." "Janet, Mary Coffman wants to borrow your tennis shoes. Leave in room 5." "Susan, you're to take fruit jello to the potluck this Sat." "Louis, the man called from Sears Roebuck. Says he'll have to send away for a new part." "Danny, you left your rubbers over at Tippy's house."

The desk is also the place for the more unpleasant communications that arise, I trust, in every household. Such as "Daddy, please check my arithmetic," or "Mother, I told Sister Jude you'd be glad to make two dozen brownies for the bake sale," or "Daddy, please fill out this Fire Prevention sheet so our room can be 100%," or "Mother, *where* are all my white socks?" or "Daddy, you owe me 10¢. I had to buy some theme paper out of my own money."

The dining room table (that we only *eat* on at Christmas and Thanksgiving) is the official place for all financial transactions. These are generally in the form of small puddles of coins on various slips of paper reading: "Danny's milk money for school." "Janet, this is for the March of Dimes." "Susan, 35¢ for a new locker key. Next time you lose it, you pay for it."

My mother, whenever she goes away for a brief visit, always leaves notes attached to the various inanimate objects that can't plead for themselves. Such as a plaintive note by the Chinese lily on the buffet: "Water me." Or a note in the bread box reading: "This bread is for birds. Cut it up small. Throw in driveway." (My mother, as you may gather, carries on the St. Francis of Assisi activities in our home. She also has scant confidence in her daughter's solicitude for the plants and the sparrows.)

There is no sign entitled "Communications from Hollywood" on the stairway post but that's the official place, just the same, for my daughters' mail. The minute they step in the house they both rush madly to the post to collect the day's haul of autographed pictures. They never, of course, get more than a routine "Sincerely yours" from a Judy Garland or a Bing Crosby but some of the minor league players seem pathetically grateful for *any* sort of a public. Such as the card Janet received just the other day from a smiling cowboy and his smiling horse: "Howdy Folks! That sure was nice of you to ask for the picture, and we hope you'll like the one I'm sending from out here in this corner of the West. Soon we'll be looking at you from the Silver Screen. Until then, the best of luck. Sincerely, Whip Wilson." (No comment from the horse.)

Along around the first week of December, various unsolicited lists begin to crop up like mushrooms after a heavy rain. These are carefully but carelessly planted in strategic spots for us to stumble across: such as this communication, so prettily depicting the true spirit of Christmas, that I found by my coffee cup:

What I Want For Christmas

Angora sweater. (Please let me pick it out.)
Corduroy skirt. (Please let me pick it out.)
Diary with key. (Brown cover. $3.00. First floor at Robertson's.)
Figure skates. (Of course I would have to be along.)
Victrola records. ("My Heart Cries For You"—"Slaughter On Tenth Avenue"—"Bring Back The Thrill." But maybe you better let me pick these out. You wouldn't know what singers I like.)

Your loving daughter, Susan.

And then there was the program of events, laboriously
worked out to the split second, that Janet recently submitted
to me. After reading it, I knew—beyond a shadow of a doubt
—that we had a budding General MacArthur in the family, for
no military invasion was ever better planned.

Plans For Birthday Party

3:30 Guests will arrive.
3:35 Take coats up to my room. Monkey around.
3:45 Come downstairs. Sit on davenport and open presents.
4:00 Play movie star guessing game. Give prize.
4:10 Guess number of beans in jar. Give prize.
4:20 Play drop clothespins in bottle. Prize.
4:30 Mother, put cake with lighted candles on table.
4:32 Make wish, blow out candles. Sing?
4:45 Serve cake, ice cream, Cokes. Buffet style. Eat in living
room.
5:15 Finish eating.
5:20 Give door prize for lucky number.
5:25 Go upstairs for coats.
5:30 Say goodbye to guests. (Daddy, could you drive Josephine home? She lives clear across town.)

All of these various communiqués are of a deciduous or
seasonal nature but there are also the more or less permanent
placards around the house. Such as the one that is scotch-
taped to Susan's bedroom door: "Do not enter unless Urgent.
Then knock and wait for a Come-in." The sign on Janet's door
doesn't make me feel *quite* so much like a chambermaid but
it is, in its way, equally intimidating. One month it may read:
"Art studio of Janet Hasley." The next month: "Dressing
room of Janet Hasley, Metropolitan Opera Star."

A somewhat less glamorous placard (the fifth line of which reads "GMIOWPX") is the Snellen eye chart that hangs in the breakfast room. This is for the benefit of my husband as he practices his "Sight Without Glasses" exercises every evening. It also serves, of course, as a free clinical check-up for any guest who is visiting us. We do not *require* our guests to have 20-20 vision, you understand, but we feel that it's only hospitable to offer them this service. If they can read "GMIO-WPX" with the naked eye at twenty paces, which puts them in front of the refrigerator, they can leave our home rejoicing. 20-20 vision.

Another placard, not quite so clinical, is on the sun porch. It is a large lovely sign, tacked onto a two-foot stick, and featuring a bright yellow arrow against a bright blue background. It reads simply: "To Notre Dame Stadium." I have tried on numerous occasions to get rid of this thing but my young son, aged six, clings to it as his dearest possession. He cannot, as a matter of fact, understand why I don't stick it out in the front yard. Don't all the cars from Chicago go past our house to the football games? (Alas, my son, they do. But let's let Notre Dame handle its own traffic problems.)

This reminds me, by the way, of one of young Daniel's first attempts at the written word. He not only carefully and accurately printed out a "For Sale" sign but hammered it onto our front door. If the people across the street had a sign, why couldn't we?

Since this early attempt, however, he has branched into more creative efforts. Such as the highly metaphysical notation I found the other week on the back of his coloring book: "Black is black. White is white. Flesh is flesh." That business about the flesh quite startled me—it seemed so mellow a reflection for one just six—and then I realized he meant *flesh colored.* Another fragment I ran across, on the back of a holy card, went: "I love God very very very much. Do you like him? You better." But I feel that his prize effort, to date, is the thumbnail sketch of his mother (who is not mechanical-minded) that he recently felt goaded into composing: "When I ask my mother questions about engines she does not answer very quickly."

All in all, I feel that it is only a matter of time before young Daniel will, like the rest of the family, be leaving notes on the living room desk. When the day comes that I find a "Mother all the kids but me have a squirt gun they only cost 25¢," I will know that he has, as a Hasley, come of age.

Swing Low,
Sweet Chariot

IT IS A fearful and wonderful thing to have a saint bud forth on one's family tree. It is especially fearful and wonderful when this budding takes place on a family tree like mine: a tree that was originally a sturdy Canadian Catholic oak but is now a strange hybrid growth that defies classification. This is not to imply that dry rot has set in or the sap run dry, during this past generation, but simply that the sap now runs rampant in all directions.

At this stage, it is almost impossible to tell—without a program—just what relatives are apostates by choice, pagans by circumstances, returned black sheep, converts, or original charter members of the Faith of Our Fathers. It is particularly difficult to track down since all the relatives have their *own* stubborn versions.

Take my Uncle John. Uncle John (God rest his soul, for he died a violent death when the automobile he was jacking up came down on his neck) was out of the Church some fifty-odd years. Yet if someone would ask, speculatively: "Let's see.

How long was it *you* were out, John?" he would always answer
indignantly, "Never *was* out. Just didn't *go*."

And then there are the dubious cases like Uncle Gilbert out
in Salt Lake City. Did he or did he not make a deathbed return? We have only his wife Maggie's description of his last
moments and, from her report, it sounds like a free-for-all.
Gilbert demanded a priest and she, Maggie, retorted, "Over
my dead body" and sent in her Lutheran minister instead.
Gilbert took one look at him and yelled: "Get out, you! I said
I wanted a *priest*!" and expired shortly thereafter.

With a family like this (recording angels working over-
time, trying to keep the files straight), there is nothing like a
family funeral—with all split factions assembled under one
roof—to make the very angels hold their breath. The Protestants stubbornly send flowers to the Catholic funerals, knowing full well that Mass cards are desired, and the Catholics
even more stubbornly deluge the bereaved Protestants with
spiritual bouquets.

The Catholics have even been known to regard, with a cold
and cynical eye, the occasional Protestant attempts to conform
to Catholic protocol. I distinctly remember the time that a wire
arrived from a wealthy, but notoriously tight-fisted, Protestant
branch of the family: "ARRANGE FOR A MASS FROM ALL
OF US HERE IN DENVER. SEND BILL."

The Catholics looked at each other. What, exactly, did
Denver have in mind? "If they're splitting expenses," said one
dryly, "a one dollar Low Mass would come to twenty cents
per head. Think they can swing it? Or should we make it a five
dollar High Mass, with music, and *really* make it hurt?"

In other words, there are times when the family charity
falleth not as the gentle rain from heaven but as a splattering
of hailstones. It is indeed fortunate that the various priests

and ministers and Christian Science readers, who have to deliver the family funeral sermons, aren't too aware of their mixed breed audiences. *If* aware, I strongly suspect that they would call it quits with a hasty "May he (she) rest in peace" and run for their lives.

Take the unfortunate case of my Aunt Agnes, who not only slid under the Catholic wire at the zero hour, but was born with—and died with—a razor-edged tongue. The priest was not, understandably enough, too well acquainted with Aunt Agnes and so, wildly grasping at the nearest straw, he based the entire eulogy on her name. Agnes, said he, meant lamb. Warming to his theme, he then went completely overboard in extolling her endearing and lamb-like qualities.

After that, the Protestants were more anti-clerical than ever. It just went to show, said they, that Catholics could bribe their priests into doing *anything*.

Fortunately, it is up to God—not us—to render final judgments on the washed and unwashed but it's certainly difficult to refrain from helping Him. The Protestant relatives, for instance, can't help speculating as to how the Catholic Cannibal on the family tree made out at heaven's gates. It seems that during the French-Indian wars, great-great Uncle Pierre was invited to a banquet by Pontiac, the big Indian chief. The meat was especially excellent and Uncle Pierre, wiping his lips, said as much to his host. Pontiac agreed and then, pointing to a burlap bag on the ground, remarked carelessly: "The rest is in there. You can have it if you like." Gluttonous Uncle Pierre, upon peering into the bag, discovered the bloody and severed head of an Englishman. (N. B. This may be verified by browsing through the historical records at Lansing, Michigan. One of my foolhardy relatives, hoping no doubt to unearth royal blood, browsed into *this* instead.)

It has not, however, been established that Pierre ate the Englishman on a Friday and so the Catholic descendants are inclined to take a lenient view of the matter. Not that they necessarily *approve* of eating one's friends but, after all, Uncle Pierre didn't actually know the Englishman by name.

The Catholics also find it easy to overlook the Catholic Smuggler in our family—my own grandmother, who smuggled her new wedding bonnet across the Detroit river under her hoop skirts. On the other hand, they entertain grave doubts about Protestant Uncle Ralph's salvation. Throughout his entire life, dour Uncle Ralph—whenever anyone asked how he was feeling—had only one standard rejoinder: "Oh, God, but I'm miserable." Even if you posed the question while he was in the thick of a spirited horseshoe game, you could still count on him to stop, put his hand to his back, and mutter, "Oh, God, but I'm miserable." Somehow, we can't quite picture Uncle Ralph in heaven because he would be so utterly miserable being utterly happy.

As I was saying, it is a fearful and wonderful thing to have a saint bud forth on a family tree like this. It is also very heartening. Even though it may never happen again, we *do* have this powerful representative—Sister M. Vera, alias my Aunt Bessie—to plead for us in the heavenly courts.

That our family should even have *produced* a nun is miraculous enough (after all, five out of her own eight brothers and sisters left the fold) let alone a truly saintly one. Oh, I grant you that our family saint will never be officially canonized but I could, if Rome wanted, furnish several pretty convincing miracles on her behalf.

Miracle #1, I think, is that Sister Vera, during her lifetime, was like the three young men in the Fiery Furnace: she, alone, walked unscathed among the fiery relatives. The well-loved baby of the family, no fiery darts ever licked at *her* black serge skirts. Indeed, in her presence, the relatives lay down, side by side, like little lambs.

Male relatives, before visiting her in the convent parlors, thoughtfully twisted their Masonic rings around on their fingers and meekly accepted, from her hands, crocheted scapulars and holy cards. Female relatives, who hadn't spoken to each other for decades, presented a charming picture of sisterly love for her exclusive benefit.

None of which, of course, fooled Sister Vera for one little minute. For if ever anyone had her apostolate all cut out for her, and knew it, she was the one. I might also add that it was a most successful apostolate—this praying her immediate family back into the Church, not to mention the outlying suburban areas—and statistics bear me out. Of the strayed brothers and sisters, all but one have eventually trailed back home, one by one. Several converts (one being myself) have emerged from the damaged suburban areas although, at the time, I was only vaguely aware that my mother had a sister who was "a nun way out in California." More things are wrought by prayer, even by unknown aunts in California, than this world dreams of.

Six years ago her teaching career was abruptly cut short by a stroke of paralysis and she was sent back here to St. Mary's, the mother house, to die. Only she didn't die. She didn't die until last week and—during those six long years in the St. Mary's infirmary—she had nothing to do but sit in a chair and continue her apostolate of prayer. Only, to prayer was now added suffering. And, to suffering, was added the irresistible touché: a complete and cheerful submission.

When asked how she was feeling (with two grotesquely swollen legs and a useless left arm), she'd pass it off with a

"Well, can't say as I've been doing any handsprings lately but now tell me how *you've* been. Has that head cold of yours cleared up?"

And her one complaint (only it wasn't so much a complaint as a sort of wistful sigh) was an occasional: "I'm so good for nothing that I can't see what's keeping the good Lord. Why doesn't He come and get me?"

In the meanwhile there was nothing to do but go on a-sitting: with the view from her window (the laundry smoke stack) and a pot of African violets, on the windowsill, for companions. The Real Companion, of course, was in the room right next to hers—the infirmary chapel—where she managed to drag herself, literally inch by inch, for daily Mass. "Maybe if they'd strap me on roller skates," she'd say, "I could manage this a little more gracefully."

About ten days ago they found her on the floor. She must have been slightly conscious for she fumbled at the cord around her waist, trying to help them loosen her clothing. In any event, it was her last conscious gesture. The priest anointed her just as she was, right there on the floor, expecting her to die any second. They went on expecting her to die any second for all of the next week (in an oxygen tent and with a temperature that soared to 107 degrees) and Sister Vera herself, if conscious in her Fiery Furnace, would probably have said: "Heavenly days, *now* what can be keeping the good Lord?"

I, myself, would be loath to interpret dogmatically the inscrutable ways of God, but Aunt Dorie didn't hesitate for a minute. Across the bed of the dying, she looked at her brother Andrew (the lone remaining "black sheep") and then put on the heat. "*You* know why poor Bessie can't die," she said reproachfully. "She's waiting for *you* to come back."

(Poor Andrew! Ex-altar boy, with his Masonic ring twisted

around for the occasion, standing helpless and clumsy in Catholic territory. And, to add to his discomfort, having various nuns come up and gently press his hand: "Ah, you must be Andrew. Sister Vera has told us *all* about you.")

"S-sh," said Mother Superior. "Maybe she can hear you for all we know. The sense of hearing is the last to leave."

"Then why don't you *all* be quiet?" spoke up Protestant Aunt Gertrude from her post by the radiator. "Why not let Bessie die in peace and quiet?"

Well, Bessie died in peace and quiet, in the small morning hours, and at last could have her lighted holy candles. (No flames, however holy, allowed near an oxygen tent.) One cannot say it was an impressive or edifying death, considering she was unconscious, but it didn't really matter at all. One who is only two inches from heaven can afford to miss out on the final liturgical farewells.

It's her funeral, though, that I really want to tell you about.

A nun's funeral is completely out of the hands of the relatives and this, I daresay, is why it is so simple and beautiful. I can't speak for the other relatives but, for me, her funeral— standing out in bright contrast to the hushed and lugubrious affairs I'd hitherto attended—lessened my own fear of death about eighty-five percent. One had only to glance at the serene and openly smiling faces of the infirmary nuns to catch the Easter spirit. (At other funerals, the "Hallelujah, He is risen" words were spoken but the fearful and stricken faces gave it the lie. Or perhaps they lacked the holy boldness to dare be happy in their belief?)

These elderly and ailing nuns would creep into the parlour and lovingly, almost enviously, pat her cheek and murmur: "Isn't she *lovely*?"

("Ye, who have understood,
Be not afraid,
Nor dread,
It is God's kiss—God's kiss that wakes the dead.")

And, over and over again, were the same refrains: "One of the most charitable nuns in the community"—"Such cheerful patience"—"Never a cross word or a complaint out of her."

(Shades of "Oh-God-but-I'm-miserable!" Uncle Ralph!)

Aunt Bessie's miracle #2, I would say, was that no relatives complained because the funeral Mass was set for 6 A.M. on the coldest day of the year—seven degrees below zero and the countryside snowbound. No one complained because there wasn't a eulogy. No one blinked an eye at having to walk around her casket in order to reach the communion rail. No one raised an indignant eyebrow because the pallbearers were just the community gardeners, garbed in ear muffs and lumber jackets. Only one relative insisted on sending a huge spray of carnations (that were promptly unwired and placed in a vase on a side altar). And, after the funeral, there were no possessions to be divided and argued over.

Mother Superior simply brought a big cardboard box down to the parlour and distributed the "estate" herself: some brown and faded family pictures, several crocheted doilies, a worn breviary, a thimble, one of those silly plastic Worry Birds (sent to her by a former student), and some black wooden prayer beads. Possessing nothing, she possessed everything.

To Andrew, of course, went the prayer beads. "We know," said Mother Superior, looking up at him with her bright warm eyes, "that Sister Vera would want you to have these." (Poor Andrew! Pocketing the rosary, and miserably aware of the hopeful and childlike strategy, he managed to mumble out of a tight throat: "Well, I still remember how it goes. I promise to say it once, anyway, for Bess.")

The community cemetery is just around the corner and generally the nuns push the casket, on wheels, down the narrow road themselves. This time, though, the snow was so deep that a hearse was needed. A snow plow had cleared the way, throwing up huge banks of snow on either side, and we—in cars—followed the hearse. As we drove along, the line of walking nuns had to step back into the snow drifts and stand at attention as we passed. This needled our souls almost past bearing. We felt like bloated politicians—complete with cigars and limousines—rolling down an avenue lined with frail and frozen angels. Still, an even worse sting awaited us at the cemetery.

Snow trenches had been dug between the rows of graves for the nuns to stand in, and stand they did—all three hundred of them in the bitter cold—while we, perforce, sat comfortably in our heated cars. Did I say "comfortably"? As my non-Catholic brother said afterwards: "I never felt so rotten cheap in all my life. Here I'd served in the South Pacific, even broken my neck, and I think of myself as a pretty tough guy. So here sits the tough guy in a closed car while all those nuns, just wearing shawls, stood like little tin soldiers in their trenches. Oh, I *know* we couldn't get out, that the car doors wouldn't even open against those high snow banks, but I felt like a perfect lug. I felt like rolling down the window and *diving* into a snow drift, to show those Catholics that if they could take it, I could too."

That burial service (as viewed from behind an automobile window) was a mute funeral sermon in itself, in sharp blacks and whites, depicting the Church Militant and the Church Triumphant. No need for a priest to translate it. There were the

rows upon rows of plain small crosses sticking their heads out
of the deep blanket of snow and, against this utter whiteness,
the rows upon rows of black garbed nuns. Overhead, the sun
shone down so fiercely on the snow—almost blinding in its
glittering radiance—that we had to squint our eyes against the
brightness.

Well, I suppose that our Sister Vera was just #374 in the
community—just another seed being planted in their frozen
garden—but, in our squinting eyes, we could ill afford the
planting. It stripped *us* of our lone family saint.

Yet if any of the relatives (who possibly thought it all more
fearful than wonderful) think that now they're *safe* from
prayers, with the family nun gone, they may be in for a surprise. Little do they know that crippled Sister Vera will now
be an agile triple-threat man. And little do they know that
the 1300 members of the Holy Cross community must offer
prayers not only for their deceased sister in Christ but *for her
relatives.*

Pray on, community, pray on!

Time marches on, and I would now like to add a postscript
to the above essay. I must tell you that there is now a young
Sister Vera in the community ranks: a young girl from Columbus, Ohio, whose story—when I heard it—made goosepimples
run down my spine. It seems that this girl one day happened
to pick up an essay I'd written and, her interest aroused,
ended up in a rectory taking instructions. Then, not satisfied
with just being a convert, she decided to become a nun and—
somehow or other—ended up at St. Mary's as a postulant. Not
knowing I lived in nearby South Bend—and certainly not
knowing that Sister Vera had been my aunt—it can only be

attributed to the mysterious ways of Divine Providence that *she*, my unknown convert, was given the name of Sister Vera. (A year after a nun's death, as I understand it, the name goes back into circulation.)

So one day, when this strange set of circumstances came to light, the new Sister Vera—quite overwhelmed by the truth-is-stranger-than-fiction aspects of it all—immediately got in touch with me. It was a strange sensation, meeting her in the convent parlours for the first time, and there was also a little presentation scene—so touching as to be almost awkward— that must have made Aunt Bessie smile. For I gave the new Sister Vera the flat silver watch, with "Sister M. Vera" in-scribed on it, that had belonged to our "family saint."

May I Now Present

ONE OF the nicest features about public speaking, as far as I'm concerned, is the eternal element of surprise. Almost all other forms of human suffering have an element of sameness about them—that is, at a certain pain level you either go into convulsions or die—but this merciful arrangement doesn't apply to the dry-mouthed agony of stage fright. You just *think* you're going to have convulsions or die: a form of wishful thinking that gets a person nowhere. Mother Nature, apparently figuring that death is too good for amateur public speakers, never steps in. She just lets you stand there and sweat it out for yourself.

Yet it's really uncanny, when you stop and think about it, just how much punishment the human system can take and still pull through. Standing before a microphone, you can experience everything but the actual death rattle and yet— O eternal element of surprise!—be able to walk off the platform unaided after it's all over. Fifteen minutes later you're even able to partake of a little nourishment—not, mind you, through intravenous feeding but by actually lifting a cup of hot Orange Pekoe to your own lips. Five minutes later, as the

hot tea expands your collapsed arteries and your eyes begin
to focus more clearly, you're even able to identify the yellowish blur on the tea table. The yellowish blur resolves into
jonquils—and what beautiful *beautiful* jonquils they are.
Wordsworth's heart may have leapt up as he beheld a host of
golden daffodils, a-dancing in the breeze, but it's nothing to the
leap that your heart takes. In fact, your heart would—at this
stage of the game—leap at the sight of a bunch of ragweed
stuck in a milk bottle. You see, the impact of what you've just
gone through has suddenly hit you. The speech is over; you
are still alive; the audience didn't even stone you.

As you gaze around with grateful and wonder-drenched
eyes, it's remarkable how different everything now looks. The
speaker's platform no longer resembles a scaffold, complete
with trap door. The size of the auditorium, formerly approxi-
mating St. Patrick's Cathedral, seems to have dwindled considerably. The lady who introduced you, now that you look
at her more closely, doesn't *actually* look like one of Stalin's
henchmen. Maybe she's even someone's mother. And, how
utterly fascinating is the lady on your left as she gives you a
detailed account of her last summer's trip to Rome. How you
tremble with delight as she plunges into her handbag and
hauls out a snapshot of St. Peter's basilica, taken on a cloudy
day and from a distance of about 500 yards, and explains the
small black dots in the lower left-hand corner. The small black
dots, it turns out, are some fellow pilgrims who—would you
believe it?—were from her old home town of Davenport,
Iowa. Harry, the biggest black dot, is now going to dental
college and his sister Ruth, the black dot to his left, once had
a poem published in the local paper and plans to . . .

(I wonder, did Lazarus—during those first awesome moments when he realized he was back in the land of the living

—experience the same joyful appreciation of his fellow men? Exclaim over a yellow jonquil? A cloudy snapshot?)

This painful method of recapturing a lost zest for living—and I heartily recommend it for all those who can't afford a trip to Sun Valley—is based, of course, on a very old principle. Joy through suffering. For instance, there's nothing like being trapped in an old mine shaft for 48 hours to make you discover a new and giddy pleasure in just breathing fresh air again. Or just *breathing*, for that matter.

This, as I say, is the nice feature about public speaking. I can't think of any other unless it's the fact that this joy-through-suffering is not limited to my own selfish self. The audience, upon realizing that I'm through talking and they're now free to go home, also experiences—although in a more passive degree—this same *joie de vivre*.

In this respect, not all public speakers contribute as much as I to the common weal. Other speakers are satisfied with shallow performances that merely delight, edify, inspire, and regale their audiences. After discounting their brilliance, wit, wisdom, larynx control, timing, stage presence, and a few other odd details—well, what have you got left? The audience loves the speaker, the speaker loves his audience, and the whole thing is pretty fruitless. No redemptive suffering, no sense of release, no nothing.

Even so, it would be perfectly all right with me if medical science would alleviate some of this redemptive suffering. Whatever strides medical science may have made in recent years, you're not going to catch *me* genuflecting before the Men in White until they come up with a cure for chronic stage fright. You know, Mr. Webster defines stage fright as "nervousness upon appearing before an audience" but Mr. Webster, although generally reliable, is here indulging in

the whimsical understatement. Actually, stage fright is an
affliction that combines all the worst features of lockjaw,
palsy, morning nausea, and creeping paralysis. Perhaps the
worst feature, though, is that you can't—like a sick cat—
crawl under a back porch and suffer in dignity. You have to
do your suffering right out in the open, with lots of people
watching you.

Moreover, the earth is strewn with these s.f. victims, even
though it's impossible to present actual statistics. Soul scars
are not always apparent to the naked eye. Perhaps the only
infallible way to check up on a suspect—a stage fright carrier, so to speak—would be to sneak up behind him and
suddenly yell: "It gives me great pleasure to introduce to
you this evening. . . ."

This dirty trick, however, would be on a par with locking
little children in old iceboxes and I, as a Christian, cannot
recommend it. It could unhinge a sensitive person for life.
As a Christian alternative, I suggest you just take my word
for it that every third person you meet on the street has suf-
fered or will suffer, before completing his life span, from
this dread malady.

(Are you the vice-president of some organization? If so,
what assurance do you have that the president may not be
down with pleurisy at the next meeting? Do you belong to a
study group? If so, do you think you can go on forever, just
functioning on the telephone committee, and never have to
give a paper? Have you been foolhardy enough to write
something for publication? If so, don't you realize that people
automatically expect writers also to be professional public
speakers? Yes, my friends, public speaking can creep up on
even those citizens who have led upright and abstemious

lives. It isn't necessarily a matter of just falling in with bad companions.)

Yet what, may I ask, are the Men in White doing about all this? Are there any research foundations? No. Has any case of stage fright, no matter how lurid, ever made the medical journals? No. Why, those Men in White haven't even bothered to cook up a Latin term for stage fright and this, to me, is the last indignity. For instance, I happen to know for a fact that a bright pink rash—common to babies and lasting only twenty-four hours—goes under the imposing title of *Roseola Infantum*. Would it be too much to ask, therefore, that stage fright be dignified with the title of *Roseola Adultum*? Heaven knows that I can break into rosy hives just *thinking* about a forthcoming speech.

Yet not all victims react the same way. Some people, upon facing an audience, turn ashy white—others a chartreuse—and still others a sort of battleship grey. Despite the variance in color scheme, though, they all have one symptom in common. They all shake. So, on second thought, I suppose a more comprehensive title would be *Shakeola Adultum*?

This may seem like a minor point, this insisting upon an official Latin term, but it just might be a stepping stone to medical recognition. It might even pave the way to the happy day when you can step into a Walgreen drug store and procure the proper medication, either in liquid or capsule form, for *Shakeola Adultum*. (I, personally, lean toward capsules that could be neatly stashed in one's vest pocket for emergency use . . . sort of like the way diabetics carry around a lump of sugar.)

As it stands, a Walgreen clerk—if asked for a remedy for just plain old stage fright—would probably just snicker and slide a 25¢ copy of *Be Glad You're Neurotic* across the counter. Or, worse, one of those Dale Carnegie books on how to magnetize your audience. The thing that's wrong with Dale is that he presupposes everyone *wants* to magnetize an audience. He'd be pretty disgusted, I daresay, with the scope of my ambition; namely, to be able to face an audience without having my stomach turn upside down. Whether or no the audience gets magnetized is their look-out. I'm just interested in my stomach, and this strikes me as a case for the Men in White rather than the Personality Boys.

I may, of course, be taking the wrong approach. Maybe the trouble *is* with my personality, rather than my Mexican-bean stomach, but psychiatric fees being what they are—well, I just thought it'd be cheaper the Walgreen way. I'd certainly feel pretty silly, paying a fat fee to rent a couch, if all I needed—before facing a microphone—was, say, some ground sassafras root and perhaps a wee dash of marijuana. (This is only a wild guess on my part, not being skilled in the lore of herbs and weeds, but—anything, anything, to spur on those Men in White.)

In the long interim, I suppose the only thing to do is string along with our present primitive methods of seeking relief. None of these works, incidentally, but I think they're rather interesting.

For instance, I have been told by a certain well-known and successful speaker—who, lucky dog, claims that *he* is always "sunk in lethargy" as he faces an audience—that I should count up to ten, slowly and silently, before opening my mouth. This silent counting is presumably to intimidate the audience, as it breathlessly waits for the first pearl to drop from your lips, and also give you time to recover your equilibrium. The only drawback to this method, admits my sunk-in-lethargy friend, is that in one known instance the speaker was so frightened that she couldn't remember what numbers *came* between one and ten. This so heightened her inferiority complex that her last estate was worse than her first: a possibility that *I* wouldn't dare take a chance on.

Another lady speaker whom I know follows the Gayelord Hauser method of relaxation. Just before a speech, she lies down for a half hour on an old ironing board, with her feet elevated fourteen inches higher than her head, and lets the blood rush to her brain. Why this should be beneficial, I am not prepared to state. All I know is that *I* don't need an ironing board because the blood rushes to my head the minute I hear: "And so, this evening, it gives me great pleasure . . ."

Moreover, I have never noted any particular therapeutic value in an incipient brain hemorrhage. Maybe it only works for those hardy souls who also follow the Hauser diet of yogurt, Brewer's yeast, wheat germ, and blackstrap molasses? It stands to reason, I suppose, that anyone who can stomach all *that* isn't likely to get queasy over a mere audience. Yet the price, I feel, is too stiff. I think, if you don't mind, I'll just hold out for those Walgreen capsules. (And certainly the great Caruso, who said "Each time I sing I feel there is someone waiting to destroy me," is of no help to me. He, to relieve nervous tension while waiting in the wings, would gargle with salt water, inhale Swedish snuff, down a glass of whiskey, chase it with seltzer, and eat a quarter of an apple.)

Several months ago, though, I ran across a method that struck me as having real possibilities. I happened to catch a vaudeville show in Chicago, starring this comedian called Henny Youngman, and it opened up wide vistas. This Henny Youngman character walks out on the stage with a violin, see, but never gets around to playing it. All he does is just *talk*.

Right away, I realized that here was another stage fright victim—only a very clever one. That violin, clutched in his hot little hand, was merely a symbol of safety to him—a shield of good purpose—and it also served to distract his audience. Expecting to hear the sweet strains of "Humoresque" at any given moment, the audience was too keyed up to notice his quivering Adam's apple or whether his talking made any sense. All eyes were on the violin.

After I get my own violin, for I daresay this Youngman doesn't have a patent on the idea, I fully expect public speaking to become a breeze. I am even, matter of fact, thinking of going Youngman one better. What's wrong with getting myself a nice big bass viol, eh? I could then sit down behind it, completely hidden from view, and read my notes in comfort. Maybe even have a cigarette or munch some Karmel Korn while I was about it. All the audience would be able to see would be my right arm, coming around the bass viol, with my fingers lightly and tantalizingly resting on the strings. As they waited for the first rich deep "pling" (which never comes) to come forth, I would take advantage of their distraction and get the speech out of the way.

Too, this "come out, come out, wherever you are" arrangement would spare me from those feminine speculations that now reach me, as if by mental telepathy, across the footlights: "Wonder why she ever selected *that* hat?"—"Do you suppose she knows what that shade of green does to her?"— "She looks lots older than her photograph, doesn't she?"— "I'll bet she'd die if she knew her underskirt was showing . . ."

Safe and cozy behind my bass viol, they wouldn't even know if my stocking seams were straight or not.

All in all, I think it's going to be nothing short of sensational (easily topping Evelyn and her magic violin that she— with no sense of showmanship—actually *plays*) and there's only one thing that bothers me. That is, I'm going to have to keep my figure chiseled down so as to *fit* behind a bass viol. I just may be forced to take up yogurt and blackstrap molasses after all.

I Fling the Torch

Is THERE a valiant woman in my audience? Would she like to go down in history as such? If so, let her step valiantly forward and lay her head upon the block I have prepared for her.

First, however, I must warn my eager audience that women of just *ordinary* valor need not apply. I have devised a little third-degree screening test that will make short shrift of just the rank and file type of candidate.

My woman must be a thorough Catholic (recommendation from parish priest will suffice); married at least ten years; husband still living (his own testimony acceptable); and with at least three or four children. I also insist that my candidate do all her own housework and be definitely in the middle class income bracket. Also, her nerves and general health must *not* fall in the Amazon or even the Sturdy Peasant division. She must have the average female's quota of frayed nerve ends, Blue Mondays, and days when her feet and back are simply killing her.

So far, so good. A million red-blooded women could qual-

ify. I now come to the valor hurdle: my woman must be
prepared, for the task ahead of her, to give her *all* and let the
chips fall where they may. These flying chips will require
(and here my demands grow a mite tougher) that she have
the inner vitality of Eleanor Roosevelt; the coolness-under-
fire of General MacArthur; the perseverance of Joan of Arc;
and the rugged honesty of Abraham Lincoln.

In brief, I want this gloriously valiant creature to write a
REAL book on Christian marriage: an *Inside Asia* exposé
from the female standpoint. Many noteworthy books on marriage have been written by men but, for my present purposes,
I dismiss—with airy hand—all male authorities on matrimony: be they priests, theologians, obstetricians, monks,
psychiatrists, sociologists, or even outstanding laymen belonging to the Knights of the Purple Garter. I want someone
who has *been* inside Asia.

This is not to say that I won't let my valiant woman, in
compiling her material, *consult* theologians—in fact, she
jolly well better or she'll never get an imprimatur—but I
insist that it be a firsthand, honest, searching, practical, specific, and personal exposé, leaving not a stone unturned. It
must, I fear, be written with her very life blood.

Yet, if I sound like Dracula, here's the reason. I am fed
up to the teeth with books that only skim the marital surface
—admit a problem and then run for their lives—or, worse,
assume that all marriages are made in heaven and only vary
in *degrees* of perfection and glory. It is, I maintain, downright discouraging and even frightening to pick up a book
dealing with the deep spiritual significance of the Christian
Family (reading like the Canticle of Canticles) and then com-
pare it with your own marriage: a marriage, mayhap, to a
dolt who doesn't even make his Easter Duty. It's one thing to

exalt the ideal marriage—either in prose, blank verse, or sonnet form—and quite another to assume blithely that this ideal marriage is the average norm. It makes the shattered reader feel as if her marriage isn't even *legal*, let alone Christian.

A far more sane and comforting basis from which to work comes from Father Dowling of Cana Conference fame: "There are very few good *marriages*. What you generally find are two good *people* living together."

Since I seem to have a truly remarkable faculty for making myself misunderstood, I would like to say—right here and now—that textbooks on moral theology and also straight spiritual reading, of the inspirational type, are not only excellent but indispensable. Personally, I—not being the type that's easily shattered—adore them.

But comes a point when the female reader of spiritual books says to herself: "Okay. I'm to follow in Mary's footsteps and model our home on that of the Holy Family: a fine ideal for developing virtues but not too helpful in solving specific problems. Somehow, Nazareth in the year 7 and Detroit, 1953, A.D., aren't quite the same. And Mary was *Mary*, not me, and Joseph was *Joseph*, not my Elmer. Moreover, they had only one child and that child happened to be the Son of God. All in all, the comparison is pretty thin. The Holy Family, the ideal family, becomes an extremely difficult ideal—especially if you're trying to sanctify a *difficult* marriage."

Where is the valiant woman who will not only bring it down to earth but be a Ways and Means Committee and Special Problems Coordinator all rolled into one? Where is the valiant woman who will bluntly call a spade a spade, instead of a long handled instrument for excavating purposes?

Not I, that's for sure. Not, at least, as long as I have any living relatives around. If I were to be exiled to Siberia it might be different but . . . . no, no, I am not, nor ever will be, that valiant soul. It takes all the valor *I* have even to bring up the subject. *I* but strike my little match in the darkness. To someone else I fling the torch; to someone else I pass the buck.

For one thing, I'm too keenly aware of the inevitable repercussions from such a publication. My valiant woman can take my word for it that the public will *not* maintain a detached and impersonal attitude toward the author. The public will either jump to the embarrassing conclusion that (1) the author herself is a flawless wife and mother with a 4 star marriage that runs like clockwork or (2) that all the horrible case histories she may mention are really her *own* thinly disguised problems. No one, for one little minute, is going to believe her when she starts out: "A friend of mine, whose husband is a confirmed drunkard, was at her wit's end," et cetera, et cetera.

Her *own* husband can anticipate, in the next mail, a prompt and helping hand from Alcoholics Anonymous. (Which reminds me that I'd better point out that "the dolt who doesn't even make his Easter Duty" is *not* a thumbnail sketch of Mr. Hasley.) Also, the children of my valiant lady can anticipate, on the parochial school grounds, remarks like: "My mother read *your* mother's book and she thinks it's just terrible the way she talks about you. *When* were you in reform school? *Why* did you steal that hot rod car?"

As I was saying, my woman must have valor. She must, after the book's publication, quietly compose herself for a living death. Yet all of this, I shall keep telling her, is of small import, weighed in the balance versus her real contribution to her Catholic sisters in marriage. And some day— who knows?—some ferial day in the missal may give way to the feast day of our very own U.S. Valiant Lady.

As one who hasn't the courage to write even a serious article on marriage, let alone a book, one may well question my qualifications for even urging the project. The answer is simple. I have been a regular member of the St. Ann's Discussion Group, a group of thirty fairly valiant women, for nigh on to eight years. For nigh on to eight years we have done nothing but whack away at our state of life and means of salvation: matrimony.

General report: it isn't exactly duck soup. We have enough material for twelve volumes already and this material will be handed over, free of charge, to anyone who has a truck to tow it away.

For the first few years, the group stuck to personal sanctification: theological definitions and applications of the various virtues to the housewife state, plus various treatises on Abandonment, Divine Providence, etc. I cannot, however, claim that we embraced all these doctrines without any mental qualifications or even actual doubts. (I mean, I say hastily, that the doctrines needed interpretation in the light of practical problems.)

Where, we began to wonder, did Abandonment and Holy Prudence kiss each other? In some practical cases, Abandonment sounded like taking a running jump off a 500 foot cliff, shouting: "I place my trust in God!" And what, exactly, fell into the category of "Keep My Commandments" and what, exactly, fell into the category of "Be Ye Perfect"? And, if you settled on Perfection, just how heroically generous could you be without your husband's official permission? Could you, either behind his back or over his dead body, give away *his* cloak and *his* money to the poor? (Something told us, on this point, that Holy Prudence would not come in amiss. Before sending his favorite overcoat to the stricken areas in Korea, better first mention it to him.)

Finally, the St. Ann members decided to start all over again, this time keeping everything on as practical and specific a plane as possible and working from the inner circle outward. To wit, our obligations to (1) our own souls, (2) our immediate family, (3) our in-laws, (4) our next door neighbors, (5) our parish, (6) our city, (7) the United States, and (8) the world at large.

Since we have only, to date, worked up to #5, we have not yet got around to setting the parish on its liturgical feet, putting the fear of the Lord into the city fathers, flushing the Communists out of the State Department, or sending some St. Ann delegates to the United Nations but . . . give us time. I have been told that the appearance of three determined women, banded together, is enough to strike terror to the heart of a pastor, councilman-at-large, or foreign ambassador.

Anyhow, our new approach—with one main speaker and two Devil's Advocates to badger her for practical flaws—has really opened the floodgates. If one had been a little mouse at the meetings, that little mouse could have heard any one of the following problems: frankly and publicly stated as a personal difficulty, confided in private to the friend on one's left, or disguised as a "A friend of mine was wondering" conjecture. Of course, if one had a personal spiritual director these problems could be easily settled outside of court. (It was generally conceded that the Saturday afternoon confessional, with waiting line, was not the ideal spot to bring up an involved problem with a priest who didn't know you from Eve.) This very point, however, brings us to question #1 in the Spiritual Division:

SPIRITUAL DIVISION:

1. I very much need, and would like, a spiritual director but my husband thinks it silly. He says his own conscience is sufficient for *him* and so mine should be, too. Must I abide by his wishes, contrary to my own spiritual good? I even have a hard time sneaking off to regular confession. If I go more than once a month he says: "Whassa matter? You murder someone?"

2. I would like to be a daily communicant but my husband says my place is at home, not in church. However, it wouldn't *honestly* interfere with my state of life or inconvenience anyone. It would only mean I would be a half-hour behind on the breakfast dishes. What difference is *that* compared to the value of the Mass?

3. My husband, on the contrary, wears me out with *his* Catholic enthusiasms. The trouble is that he gets the original inspiration but all the work falls on me. Right now, he's got the "back to the golden days of yesteryear" bug and I just don't *want* to keep a cow in the garage and churn my own butter.

Since, unfortunately, the correct offhand answer to these nice little problems is: "Better abide by your husband's wishes, sister," the next logical question is: "How can I enlighten or get around my wayward husband, who has not had the benefit of the St. Ann's group?" This leads us, naturally, to the Difficult Husband Division.

DIFFICULT HUSBAND DIVISION:

1. How can I, aside from prayer and example, get my husband to the sacraments? Since nagging is taboo, what *subtle* method might I use? (Our prize-winning suggestion from the floor was to have the wife say subtly: "Dear, I left the car parked in the driveway in case you were planning on going over to confession tonight.")

2. This may sound funny but my husband seems almost jealous of God. My newly-awakened interest in my faith makes him uneasy and disturbed. We have always been very close to each other and he seems to think "religion" will take me away from him; that I'm sailing off to another world. How can I not only reassure him but possibly wake him up, too?

DIFFICULT NEIGHBOR DIVISION:

1. My elderly neighbor, who hasn't a radio, comes over to my house every morning to listen to the Jehovah Witness hour. It's driving me crazy, trying to show religious tolerance and neighborly love. *Must* I put up with the Jehovah Witness hour?

2. If a guest in your home comes out with some atrocious and prejudiced remarks against Negroes, what should you do? Remonstrate? Maintain a reproachful silence as you calmly pour him another cup of tea? Hit him over the head with the teapot?

DIFFICULT CHILDREN DIVISION (That could go on indefinitely):

1. Our children only meet and play with other Catholic children and, by now, they have a very warped viewpoint.

They regard all others as "untouchables." If a stranger comes to visit us, they immediately hiss: "Is he a *Catholic*?" My husband considers this a fine militant attitude. I consider it obnoxious.

2. Our sixth grade child comes home with theological statements that are absolutely not true—namely, labeling everything in sight a mortal sin. I have verified this situation with a number of other parents and so I can't go on forever saying: "Darling, you must have misunderstood Sister." Should I give Sister a book on Canon Law for Christmas?

3. How does one go about instilling a little of the joy of Holy Poverty and the dignity of manual labor into a teen-age daughter?

4. What if all your children are responsive toward various liturgical practices—such as Advent Wreaths, family rosary, family singing, etc.—except one? And that one child, with his jeers, wrecks the whole thing?

HOUSEWORK DIVISION:

1. Marriage authorities say we should maintain a reasonably clean and comfortable home. What, exactly, does "reasonably" mean for busy and harassed mothers? (Our prize-winning definition: A reasonably clean and comfortable home for harassed mothers is where your feet don't stick to the kitchen linoleum and where your husband can make his way through the living room without breaking his leg.)

2. Am I justified in using prepared cake and biscuit mixes—that my husband loudly professes to abhor—if he actually can't tell the difference?

SEX DIVISION:

1. My husband has a deflected septum in his nose that can't be corrected. His snoring keeps me awake night after

night. I love my husband, septum and all, but am I justified in permanently moving to the guest room? (Prize-winning suggestion: Buy some wax ear-plugs, costing only 25¢, at your nearest drug store. Since these are effective even in noisy automobile plants, they should at least muffle the sound of the snoring.)

2. A friend of mine was wondering just what are valid reasons for refusing one's husband his marital rights? (Answer: Mighty few, mighty few. Insanity, T. B., complete intoxication, etc. A mild glow from a couple of beers—or even an onion sandwich—doesn't count.)

3. I honestly can't figure out what constitutes "impure thoughts" for a married woman—providing, naturally, there's no other man on the horizon. By the way, is it mental unfaithfulness to get all melty over the movie love-making of, say, Gregory Peck?

FINANCE DIVISION:

1. I would like another child, before it's too late, but my husband thinks we can't afford it. Must I let him win out on this?

2. I sympathize with my husband's financial jitters but he worries, constantly and out loud, in front of the children. It's giving them a terrible, and also unjustified, sense of insecurity along with an undue reverence for money. He even ruins our meals by demanding: "How much did these pork chops cost tonight?" and then choking when I tell him. How can I instill a little more of the "Be not solicitous for the morrow" into him?

Well, there you have it: sample problems, pulled at random, from my files on the Christian Family. Some of them sound silly, some of them near-tragic, but—since smiles and tears often trip over each other—I think they all deserve thoughtful answers. How climb that ladder to the ideal marriage when some of the lower rungs are broken or even missing?

Pardon me a minute, please. Some man in the balcony is trying desperately to get the floor. What's that you say, Mister? Oh. He says that most of these silly old problems I've mentioned could be cleared up in just one man-to-wife chat over the breakfast table.

Audience, don't look now but there's that thickheaded optimist again—assuming that both husband and wife share the same Christian principles and to the same degree. That's *precisely* the basis for most of these silly old problems. And while I hate to say this, it's generally true that women are more "spiritual-minded" than men and it's up to them to lead the way delicately. Nor does this delicacy mean saying, in a hearty voice, over the breakfast table: "See here, my good man. I've decided to make a Christian out of you. Any last requests before I start in?" The average male, bless his heart, would be over the back fence and on his way without even finishing his coffee.

A more practical, and also more polished method might be first to drop a sedative in his coffee and then say: "Dear, I have to write a paper for the St. Ann's on the spiritual significance of the Christian Family. You always phrase things so well—and I'm so very stupid at it—that I was wondering if *you* wouldn't like to collect the material and write it for me? Gosh, dear, I'll bet you'd be a perfect whiz in theology if you ever went into it. In fact, I've often wondered why *you* didn't start a St. Andrew's Discussion Group. . . ."

Would that valiant woman like to pick up the ball and carry on from here? The need is urgent because St. Paul— with his edict that a wife is subject unto her husband—forgot to leave us wives any helpful off-stage directions. Life with father must have been different in the days of Paul of Tarsus.

Jeanmaire, Jeanmaire!

JEANMAIRE, THE French premiere ballerina, recently enriched my newspaper reading by consenting—in a Hollywood press interview—to give her views on American wives. I would like to quote, if you can bear it, one of the more fascinating paragraphs:

" 'I think life here in America is easier for women because they are more spoiled,' Jeanmaire said, after a thoughtful pause. 'I don't say they deserve it, but they get so much attention from their husbands.' "

After a thoughtful pause on *my* part, I hauled out my typewriter. "Jeanmaire, Jeanmaire!" I said to myself, as I settled down at the keyboard. "I got some news for you, honey."

To begin with, Jeanmaire, I think you should know that Indiana (which is one of the forty-eight states and legally recognized as part of America) was settled by strong pioneer stock—from which I spring—and that the womenfolk underwent great hardships. Toiling slowly across the flat open plains in ox-pulled covered wagons—dodging the Indians—depending on wild game and fish for sustenance—cooking over open kettles—fighting off buzzards with only their sun-bonnets—

It was a hard life, Jeanmaire, and I want you to know that things out here in Indiana haven't improved too much. For instance, my husband—and you'll be hearing more about *him* shortly—still feels the need to supplement our food supply by fishing. You'll also, shortly, be hearing more about *that*. Anyway, I could put up with this rude primitive existence, as what real woman couldn't, if only my husband still loved me and showered me with little attentions. Something more, you know, than just bringing home bluegills and an occasional bullhead.

My first intimation, Jeanmaire, that my husband—after sixteen years of married life—was no longer madly in love with me, came in the summer of '51. We were at Lake Wawasee and I remember the scene perfectly. We were out on the lake; the sun was just sinking; the water lapped gently against the rowboat.

"This is the end!" said my husband, as he jabbed a fat juicy catalpa worm, that squirted in all directions, onto my fishing hook. "Sixteen years of this is enough! Starting as from now on, Sister, you're going to bait your own hook."

I paled. "You can't do this to me," I said, in a husky voice. "I'll fight you, I'll fight you in every court in the land. I'll carry this thing to the Supreme Court if necessary. I'll. . . ."

He handed me my pole. "You wouldn't have a chance," he said. "Pah, a grown woman who won't bait her own hook! Why, there isn't a judge in the country who wouldn't uphold me. I'll bet they'd even award me the children without so much as—Hey! *Don't* throw your line right on top of mine. Throw it out on the other side."

So. *Now* he didn't even want me on his side of the boat, our fishing lines intimately tangled together. This was what came, I thought—as I crouched, brooding and sullen, over my pole—of trying to be a Good Sport and pretending to share my husband's passion for fishing. Why, only three weeks before (unfortunately, Jeanmaire, college professors get long summer vacations), I'd found myself in the wilds of Canada . . . being a Good Sport in a 2×4 cabin with a kerosene lamp and outdoor plumbing . . . while it rained for three solid days. And for why? To catch fish. To provide sustenance.

Oh, sure, I'd heard some people refer to fishing as a "sport" and as "recreation" but I'd never put any stock in the report. Surely, men were only driven to fishing because of sheer hunger? Nor did I put any stock in that highly suspicious endorsement of fishing that was attributed to Allah: "Allah does not deduct from the allotted time of man those hours spent in fishing." It was certainly shortening *my* life span and I felt that Allah . . .

"For heaven's sake," said my husband, interrupting my Mohammedan meditations, *"why* don't you ever check your bait?"

I gave a little jump. "Oh, I'm sure it's fine," I said nervously. The catalpa worm had probably dissolved long ago but who was I to hasten the evil hour when I'd have to replace it? "Look," I went on, to divert him, "isn't the sunset pretty now? I mean, all that purple and pink. . . ."

"Look at your bait!" he roared, sounding like Captain Queeg in *The Caine Mutiny*. "Don't you *want* to catch a fish?"

And have it eat up the worm? Don't be silly, I thought.

Besides, catching a fish might now be dangerous on other grounds. Now that my husband no longer loved me, the next edict would probably be that I even had to—oh, he couldn't, he *couldn't*. What man, with even a shred of chivalry, would expect a woman to remove the hook from the bloody and mutilated jaws of a flapping fish? No man. Except possibly my husband?

I quelled the mutiny rising in my bosom long enough to take a quick look at the worm. Something resembling about an inch of white slimy sewing thread, #60, still remained. I plopped it quickly back in the water and reported, cheerily, that the worm was in fine condition. Practically as good as new, no sense in wasting. . . .

"I saw it!" roared Captain Queeg. "Pull in that line! Now, what do you want to try putting on? A night crawler, a grub worm, or a catalpa?"

(Jeanmaire, I would like to repeat that I come from pioneer stock. I can, without batting an eyelash, kill spiders, cockroaches, June bugs, and centipedes. I once, at a snake farm outside of Washington, even stroked a drugged boa constrictor. I just can't stand *worms*, is all.)

"What," I now said in a faint voice, "is the skinniest thing you have? What has—urp—the fewest insides to ooze out?"

He handed me a six-inch slimy night crawler, and one look at it and you'd know why it crawled at *night*, that immediately slithered around my index finger and fell to the bottom of the boat. I could see it, between the boards, sluicing around in a half inch of dirty water. Drowning, I hoped.

"Rescue it," ordered Captain Queeg sternly. "We don't waste worms aboard this boat. Besides, you didn't even *try* to hang onto it."

Beads of sweat were standing out on my brow by the time I once again had the worm in starting position. "Now, don't act as if you were threading a needle," said this stranger in the boat with me. (Twenty-four hours earlier he had been a kind and loving husband. Now, I felt, he would stop at nothing.) "Insert the hook firmly— No!—not in the middle, near the end—all right, now!—slide the worm onto the hook—then in and out—that's it—keep pushing. So what if part of him *has* fallen off? You've still got a good four inches to work with—keep pushing—"

"I think it's dead by now," I said, after several centuries had glided by. "Can I quit? Can we go home now?"

For answer, Queeg picked up the tin of worms, gave it a knowing thump with his hand, and extracted a fresh one.

Three night crawlers, two catalpa worms, and one grub worm later (the grub having proved the winning number), I had baited a hook to suit Queeg. That is, the worm—although badly mangled—was still alive and was, all things considered, in much better shape than I. *I*—that spoiled American wife, smothered under with attentions from my husband— barely had the strength to lean over the boat and rinse the greenish-white entrails off my hands.

Jeanmaire, I had—in the past half hour—come close (or as close as I ever would come) to what is referred to as the Dark Night of the Soul. The stark stripping of the senses— the conviction of utter abandonment by both God and man —the yearning for death. Generally, I know, a soul so tested has *already* been raised to a rare degree of sanctity but— don't be too fast, Jeanmaire, in ruling me out. I'd been married, remember, for sixteen years to you-know-who.

Besides, God's ways are inscrutable. He can, in the acid testing of the spirit, use either worms or nails. And I humbly think that I, with my very first night crawler, shot through the purgative stage like Halley's comet. That I slowly emerged into the illuminative stage when I realized, on facing the catalpa, that *my* will no longer counted. That I soared into the unitive stage when I—abandoned, in darkness, with the grub worm—still did not openly rebel against God. God, who had *invented* worms.

I just rebelled, is all, against my husband. (A human being, acting like a worm, is even more despicable than the real article.) Anyway, Jeanmaire, I want you to know that I haven't baited a hook since that dark and dreadful scene at Wawasee. Translated, this means that I haven't gone fishing since. *This*, translated, means that this past summer—and high time, too—I took off on a two weeks' solo vacation: a vacation that is openly referred to, in these parts, as The Mrs. Hasley Mutiny.

But *you* understand, don't you, Jeanmaire? I mean, after all I'd gone through? How my old pioneer bones needed the healing rays of the sun on the Maryland seashore? How I needed, to restore my spirit, to be with kind and loving friends?

My husband, of course, stayed home and took care of the three children. But don't get any ideas, Jeanmaire, that he was *spoiling* me. I admit it was quite decent of him and all that, but—and this makes all the difference, as any woman knows—he didn't think of it *all by himself*. I had to suggest it.

"It may be true," I said, in a darkly suggestive voice, "that the family that prays together, stays together, but as for the family that *fishes* together—well, it just might work vice versa. You know what I mean?"

Queeg seemed to know.

"And before I die," I went on, in a voice that implied it wouldn't be long, "I'd like a vacation that's a *housewife's* idea of a vacation. I would like to stay in a swishy hotel and wallow in luxury. I would like to be as unpioneerish as possible. I would like, above all, to be a Poor Sport for two solid weeks and have nothing whatsoever to do with fish. Except, maybe, with a fork."

Well, Jeanmaire, it was a lovely vacation. I flew to New York and spent a week with kind and loving friends in Scarsdale, roughing it on a wooded estate that resembled Hyde Park. The only hardship I faced in Scarsdale was in having to carry my own tray out to the terrace one evening for a buffet supper. But what could I do, Jeanmaire? I mean, the hostess was my dearest friend and I could scarcely refuse—even though it meant hiking from the kitchen through the butler's pantry through the dining room, living room, and television room *before* reaching the terrace. The living room, of course, was the worst stretch. All *it* needed, it was so long, was some bowling pins at one end.

Exhausted by all this hiking, I rather dreaded—to tell the truth—the long trek to the seashore but it wasn't so bad. At least, it wasn't so bad as the ox-pulled covered wagon treks of my ancestors. You see, Jeanmaire, my friends and I flew down to Maryland in the company's private plane: complete with picture windows, swivel chairs, a lounge, and a telephone. So, having taken my usual Dramamine pill before flying, I was in fairly good condition when we reached the Colonial Hotel (which couldn't have been *more* colonial unless it had the Potomac flowing by instead of the boardwalk) and quite ready for the rigorous week ahead. Such as sauntering down to the dining room every morning and picking up a menu with *"Good morning!"* embossed on the cover. (*So* like home.) And then, after stowing away a five course breakfast, calling out to the beach boy to please— and step fast, boy!—set up our striped umbrellas and chairs for the day's lolling on the beach.

The only disturbing note, in this paradise enow, was the news from home. My husband was now, it seemed, maltreating our daughters. "I've been taking them fishing every night out at the Notre Dame lake," he wrote. "You should see them bait their own hooks by now. *They're* really good sports."

Resolutely ignoring this subtle jibe, I proceeded—after, that is, I'd dropped into the Star-of-the-Sea church to pray for my daughters—to enjoy my Poor Sport vacation with even more vigor. That is, lolling a little harder. I even, Jeanmaire, began to take a rather strange delight in the occasional fishy smell that came in on the evening sea breezes. It was a cozy live-and-let-live feeling, knowing the fish were safe and happy in their proper element and I in mine.

And then, Jeanmaire, it happened. We were lolling on the beach, one fine afternoon, when my dear friend's husband suddenly reared up on one elbow. "Hey, look!" he cried, his face and voice positively aglow. "Here comes a marlin boat! Three blue flags and one red. That means they've got three marlins aboard, Lu, and someone has earned a Good Sport medal."

"What d'ya mean, Good Sport medal?" I said, with a faint flicker of interest or, maybe, just because I was sensitive on the point.

"You get this little medal, see, if you catch a marlin and are good enough sport to throw it back in the sea. Come on," he said, dragging us to our feet, "let's go down and watch them land."

By the time we got there, the three marlins were strung up on exhibition although the three Poor Sports, the cads who insisted on keeping their haul, had understandably slunk away. I gazed at the eight-foot, sword-nosed, aluminum-skinned marlins with a speculative eye. What, I asked myself, would I ever want with a marlin? What could be *less* painful than to part with the creature, heave it right overboard again? Ergo, what *easier* way could I possibly find to redeem myself, in my husband's eyes, and be hailed as a Good Sport?

For the first time in my life, Jeanmaire, I felt a burning urge to go fishing. There was just one thing that bothered me. "Would the man," I asked, "bait the hook for me?"

"Certainly!" was the answer. "In fact, he'd insist on it. Of course, Lu, it costs seventy-five dollars to hire the yacht."

The price seemed negligible—a mere pittance, in fact, to pay the nice man for baiting my hook—and look what I'd have! A little medal. Surely, I reasoned, my husband would be only too happy to wire me the necessary money.

Jeanmaire, I know you'll find this hard to believe—even after all I've told you about Queeg—but he flatly refused to send me a penny. He wasn't, he said, paying any seventy-five dollars so I could throw a fish overboard.

So now you know, Jeanmaire. I mean, how American husbands really treat their wives and how—when it comes to a seventy-five dollar showdown—you can't say much for their sportsmanship, either.

Load that Plate, Lift that Fork!

I GUESS YOU might say that my personal contribution to Negro advancement has been *eating*. For the past seven years, I—on behalf of racial justice and understanding—have been steadily eating my way through calory-loaded salmon rings, hot pecan rolls, shrimp creole, fudge cake, Hungarian kieflies, pizza pie, and various other exotic delicacies that would make the Trappists blanch. (*They*, I'm beginning to suspect, are not exactly on the side of gluttony and soft living. They've taken the high road; I've taken the low road; and small wonder if they reach Scotland afore me. Can't travel fast on an overloaded stomach, you know.)

The point remains that there's practically no delicious delicacy that I won't eat, for the love of Christ and His Mystical Body, and let no one sneer at my apostolate. As my girlish figure grows less and less girlish, I can't for the life of me see that I'm one whit less heroic than the more ascetic type of apostle. Just enjoying my heroism more, that's all.

Perhaps I should make clear, however, that the constitution of our Blessed Martin group in South Bend, where all this interracial feasting takes place, does not officially list food as its prime purpose in life. Rather, our constitution has all the high-minded and breathless beauty of the Gettysburg Address. Neither is Duncan Hines, that gourmet of the U.S. highways, our patron saint.

In brief, there is method in our gastronomical madness. And if my readers can quit drooling over that shrimp creole and fudge cake for a few minutes, I'll be happy to explain everything.

Once upon a time I belonged to a sternly ascetic Catholic study group composed of Notre Dame faculty wives. It was a very zealous-for-Christian-wisdom little group and it was really a shame therefore when we met with an untimely end. (Moral: Don't bite off more than you can chew, even if you *do* belong to the Superior White Race. We bit off a goodly sized hunk of St. Thomas Aquinas, with no one to assist us in the chewing maneuvers, and this was our undoing. The group folded up from sheer exhaustion.)

Yet for some of us, in spite of our weakened condition, there remained a nostalgic sense of loss. It *had* been a good group, hadn't it, until Aquinas came along?

Then, one fine day, several of us nostalgic souls happened to hear the Chicago Friendship House Director give a lecture on race discrimination and segregation. She must have been fairly eloquent because, before she'd even left town, my friend Katie Dooley and I had concocted what we felt was the greatest little scheme since Lincoln freed the slaves.

The Friendship House lady appeared to think otherwise. She seemed to think that Katie and I, with our raw and reckless enthusiasm and no experience, would probably set the Cause back a good ten years. Not to mention setting off some very fine race riots.

Our little scheme was simply to kill two birds with one stone. First bird: we were getting lonesome for the word of God and would like to start another study group. Second bird: we would make it a mixed membership—half white, half colored—and thus put that word of God into action. Moreover, we would hold our fortnightly meetings in EACH OTHER'S HOMES—not a safe neutral ground like a church basement—and make it a real acceptance all the way round. If colored women trooping into our homes proved a bad jolt to the neighbors, in our restricted white neighborhoods, it would be a *good* bad jolt. And this jab at segregation, however puny, was something not even Friendship House workers could imitate. We had the edge on the professionals because *we* had private homes to fling open. We also, if I may say so, were fairly respectable and solid citizens and wouldn't be brushed off by the cynical as either "paid social workers" or "radical religious crackpots." Just local citizens gone slightly berserk, shall we say?

As to the hundred and one touchy situations and complications that would no doubt arise among ourselves—such as the difference in backgrounds and education—well, we figured that the thing to do was just to close our eyes, make the sign of the cross, and jump in. What man, by just taking thought, can infallibly predict what the morrow will bring? No man. For as Charles Péguy, in his poem called *Abandonment*, has God say:

". . . But the man who, going to bed at night, makes plans for the next day,

That man I don't care for.

Jackass, how does he know what tomorrow will be like?

Does he even know what color the weather is going to take on?

He had much better say his prayers. I have never withheld tomorrow's bread.

The man who is in my hand like the staff in the traveller's hand,

That man is agreeable to me, says God."

The main drawback to this beautiful application of Abandonment was that we didn't have even a nodding acquaintance with any colored women. (There were certainly none to nod at in *my* parish church.) We could scarcely run an ad in the local *Tribune*: "Wanted, a half-dozen Catholic colored women who would like to become friends with a half-dozen Catholic white women." But wait! Might not Father Vincent Thilman, C.S.C., the white pastor of Saint Augustine's church, be game to round up some equally game souls among his colored flock?

He was not only game but enthusiastic. So over a luncheon table (already I was beginning my eating apostolate) we laid the groundwork. Father Thilman offered to be our chaplain and faithfully attend all meetings and, after that magnificent gesture, the Friendship House lady gave us her rather shaky blessings. "It's a lovely idea, just lovely. It's just that it's never been tried before and I—um—ah—well, the Holy Ghost be with you."

Both the Holy Ghost and Blessed Martin must surely have been hovering solicitously over that first meeting we held in Katie's living room in Harter Heights. As Katie, who was really the master brain behind everything, has described it elsewhere: "The colored women brought what one of them described as a certain amount of apprehension and a great deal of reserve. The white women brought a somewhat nervous desire to be gracious and an even more nervous fear of being distastefully over-gracious. All of us brought blundering good will and a sincere determination to *do* something about racial understanding. These awkward gifts were accepted by the powers-that-be and, in return, we were handed a totally unexpected boon: the gift of laughter."

It was that laughter, based perhaps on everyone's jumpy and yet good-natured awareness that we were treading on egg shells, that really launched us. Someone pulled a boner and, in the spontaneous shout of convulsive mirth that went up, the tension evaporated into thin air for keeps. Over the past seven years, I would say that this quick and easy humor on both sides, that keeps forever bubbling to the surface, has been the chief characteristic of our group. What an almost miraculous blessing was this: that in a hastily assembled group of strangers we didn't draw a single Bellicose Bertha or Gloomy Gertie! Still, I don't think they could have stayed that way for long with a priest like Father Thilman around. He's the sort of person who—when he's tickled, which is fre-quently—gives a sharp helpless howl and slaps his leg like the end man of a minstrel show. (An expression that would have made me bite my tongue in those early race-conscious days but now, glory be, would pass unnoticed. Which shows how far we've come along the way of friendship. Another indication is the way we "insult" and goof each other about individual and feminine failings: the acid test that makes or breaks.)

The other great blessing to befall us Innocents Abroad, along with the gift of impolite mirth and our wise and delight-ful chaplain, was our decision *not* to take up, in businesslike fashion, the race problem. (It was our smarter colored sisters who voted against it, even though we'd already invested in a textbook by Father LaFarge.) Instead, we decided to meet on just a sisters *under* the skin basis: Catholic wives, mothers, and homemakers. This was a wondrously wise move, as it turned out, for in this way the inevitable race grievances came up *naturally* and not in a forced or self-conscious or too belligerent fashion.

For the first few years, our group shunned publicity of any sort—after all, we had first to prove ourselves—and then we started venturing forth. We felt (somewhat reluctantly, for our nest was warm and cozy) that the time had come to appear as witnesses. For instance, our first public appearance was when we showed up at an all day Civic Rights Institute, sponsored by Jews, Catholics, and Protestants, in a local Methodist church. This Institute was a very worthwhile first step in the right direction, I kept telling myself all day, but it also tried my spirit sorely. My bored spirit had a hard time remembering that there had been a first step for me, too.

Everyone spouted elegantly but vaguely on good will and citizenship and brotherhood (carefully ignoring anything spiritual but pumping the citizenship angle as if we'd just arrived at Ellis Island) and sang little ditties like "All We Want Is A Friendly, Friendly World." Sitting stolidly in those pews, *our* little group—forgive me!—provided the living, if rather stark, example of: "We don't just talk and sing songs. We *are*."

If this smacks of spiritual pride—well, you're right. I did feel proud that day. Along with the pride I also had the sinking sensation that I was probably the most prejudiced soul in that entire crowd of five hundred assorted church women. Prejudiced, that is, in favor of the Catholic Church and its strong and unabashed supernatural approach to social issues. Shed a tear, if you will, over its unheeding members but sing alleluia for the surefooted doctrine and supernatural strength that's *there* to lean upon, anyway.

Yet in all justice to this group of assorted church women, and we are now in our fourth year of operation, I would like to say that the early vagueness has disappeared. As it now stands, it is indeed a power for good in the community and was one of the chief reasons that South Bend won the title of Brotherhood City of the nation in 1951: an award made by the National Conference of Christians and Jews. And for the benefit of those Catholics who are *leery* of joining forces with non-Catholics, I would like to quote from Father Karl Adam's book called *One And Holy*: "We do not know what is in the divine plan of salvation. But we do know that we ourselves, though we cannot create any final unity in Christendom, must do everything possible to prepare the way for dynamic unity, a unity of hearts and minds. If there cannot immediately be unity of faith, let there at least be unity of love. *And this love must and will drive us to work in common in public life and to make common cause in our social, cultural, economical and political duties and interests.* [Italics mine.] Nothing but this unity in love can provide the pre-requisite foundation for our future unity in faith. It is then not only a moral but a religious duty. As faith leads to love, so does love to faith."

If there is anything that the outside world is aware of, as regards the Catholic Church, it's the irritating (to them) dogma that one church is *not* as good as another; that Christ established but one Church; and that's us. Since outsiders bump into this irritating (to them) stand at every turn of the path, I think it's safe to assume that they're *more* than aware of the stone wall they're bucking. So, this established, what's wrong with going overboard, when it comes to friendly cooperation, in everything that's *legal*? That is, everything that does not involve matters of faith.

Somehow, my simple peasant mind can't seem to grasp the notion that Catholicism is a hothouse flower that will wither and fade away with the first rude breath from the outside world. It is even more difficult for me to see how we are supposed to go into the marketplace and be the leaven in the loaf, et cetera, without going *near* the loaf. Certainly, the Maryknoll priests would be a fine outfit if they, in order not to jeopardize their own souls, refused to budge into foreign countries. There is a certain risk involved in doing anything that's worth the doing and no one has ever said that Christianity was a nice safe proposition.

There is, on the Notre Dame campus, this very famous Lobund Laboratory where they raise germ-free guinea pigs. Everything that reaches the little pig is completely sterile and filtered from any outside contamination and it's all very marvellous, of course, from a scientific viewpoint. But we are dealing with the supernatural viewpoint in the lay apostolate and the Pope is asking for *apostles*: not a herd of guinea pigs confined to a Catholic ghetto!

Can someone please tell me, at this point, how I got off the subject? How I, in discussing our Blessed Martin group, ended up with guinea pigs? Yet it really all ties together, believe me, and was a necessary digression. There's no point in talking about brotherhood and civic projects and what-have-you without first making clear the path. In brief, I but echo the sentiment of Cardinal Suhard when he said that the worst mistake we could make would be to let the world take shape without us.

But now back to our little Blessed Martin group. We next, like lambs to the slaughter, entered our first militant skirmish: the pending public housing bill, that practically tore our city hall (in this Brotherhood City of ours!) apart. This was indeed a baptism by fire, for the bill was crushed to smithereens, but it at least opened our innocent eyes to the fact that it was prejudice against Negroes, pure and simple, that was at the basis of the crushing. Another valuable bit of training we picked up was in learning to interpret the fancy phrases that cloak cowardice, greed, and the endearing creed of "I gotta look out for myself first, don't I?"

In matters like this, a small group of housewives are no match for the city politicians and real estate clique but it's something, at least, to get up on your hind legs and howl. Maybe bite an ankle or two, especially Catholic ankles, if the opportunity arises.

What a group of housewives *can* do—we hope, we hope— is inspire and encourage other housewives, in other communities, to start their own Blessed Martin groups. Yet, while I like to think this article might be helpful toward that end, I prefer to give only a sweeping summary of our experience rather than a detailed and blow-by-blow account of the things we've worked out together. If anyone wants details, write in. We'll send you a copy of our constitution, hot off the mimeograph press, along with our blessings. We loathe red tape on principle and got along just *fine* without a constitution until outside requests started coming in. Hastily our group went into a huddle and tried to figure out just what our principles, if any, were. (Since principles weren't something you could eat, we were rather out of our natural orbit.) Still, it turned out to be fairly simple. We just looked around and saw what we

had accomplished, willy-nilly, and said: "Sure. That's what
we had in mind all along. Let's put it in English now."

Thus it is that our Purpose (not to be confused with our
more eloquent Preamble) now reads: "1. Through study of
the Catholic religion, as a common meeting ground, we hope
to grow in grace and wisdom. 2. Negro and white members
thus cooperating, we expect to attain a more complete understanding between the two races."

Just how much we've grown in grace and wisdom is something for the recording angels to judge, not us, but our
efforts have certainly been on the level. That is, the religious
study is not just a false front, a make-shift meeting ground
for the racial purpose. (On the contrary, a group like this
affords an ideal way to imbibe Christian truths because the
race consciousness adds zest and point and poignancy to the
various doctrines.) Too, the colored members are all converts, with non-Catholic husbands, and the majority of us
whites are also adopted children: hence a general need and
desire to "increase in grace and wisdom." To help us along
the way, we've had the cream of the Notre Dame clerical crop
for retreats and special talks, not to mention all the outside
speakers—such as Father Gerald Vann, to name but one—
who have come to us out of the love of God. Or free of charge,
to put it more sordidly.

None of our material, incidentally, is watered down for the
benefit of those with less formal education. (Which reminds
me, lest you think we're terribly lop-sided in this respect,
that it so happens we have two Masters' degrees in our group:
one belonging to a colored, one to a white member.) We *are*
careful, however, to avoid—like a plague—anything long-
winded or dull or pedantic: an excellent formula, if you ask
me, for any group, any color, any race, any sex.

We also go in heavily for social "side excursions" although the element of edification behind our fine Southern hospitality should be obvious to all. Such as the annual big tea we give for the nuns of Saint Mary's and the local parochial schools; the annual big picnic, held at a local park, in order to bring our children together; meeting downtown together for lunch at a large "white man's land" tea room. Aside from the occasional rubber-necking that takes place, no unpleasant incident has ever occurred. After all, we *are* ladies and we brandish nothing more dangerous than our raised forks.

So! Let no one think, for one little minute, that we are doggedly pursuing our way, secretly bored to death, but enduring it all for the Cause. Rather, the Cause—for which we were *prepared* to burn at the stake—has handed us so much downright fun that it doesn't quite seem orthodox. We've had wonderful times together and I can honestly say, with my hand on the new Knox Bible, that I've never enjoyed any group in my whole life as much as this. Nor am I alone in my sentiments. Not a single member has, over the years, relinquished her membership: come illness, new babies, household dilemmas, or bigger and better apostolic fields.

Correction: we *have* lost a member, in body, but not in spirit. Emma, the wife of a colored doctor, had been on the ailing list for some time and then came the day when our chaplain gathered us together at her home to say the rosary for her. "But won't that make her feel like she's dying?" I asked, quite horrified. "But she *is* dying and she knows it," he answered. "I want you to go in and congratulate her on being the first Blessed Martin to make heaven."

It was a nice assignment, all right. Emma had been a big and large-boned woman with a forthright honesty and bluntness that had always tickled us. At every meeting, precisely at eleven o'clock, she would get to her feet and say: "I'm tired. I want to go home." Now, as we entered her bedroom to say goodbye, and offer our congratulations, we found that Emma—riddled with cancer—was little more than a shell. Her eyes, liked glazed marbles, seemed sightless. I knelt down beside this shell and patted her hand. "This is Lucile," I said, in one of the most difficult gestures of my life. "Will you remember me when you get to heaven?"

Out from this shell, surprisingly enough, boomed the same old strong voice of Emma. "I remember you," she promised, with all the firmness with which she used to say, "I'm tired. I want to go home."

But to get back to the live members. It's quite obvious, I daresay, that we rather like ourselves. Yet has a group like this any intrinsic value in itself (outside of what *we've* gained) or any far-reaching influence?

Actually, we're very small peanuts and we know it. Yet I feel that a community group like this, that strikes in a personal way at prejudice based on "human feelings," has every bit as much value, in its own way, as the most triumphant passing of any civil rights legislation. The point is that laws can force people but not convert them, and legal justice—grudgingly executed—can be a cold and heartbreaking thing: somewhat like handing a fellow human being a crust of bread on the end of a ten foot spear. There are also too many snide and tricky ways of getting around laws.

So it's pretty important to strike at prejudice right where it hurts: the personal contact.

I have a very strong hunch that lurking behind the elaborate network of anti-Negro generalizations (lazy! shiftless! amoral! primitive! illiterate!) is the simple aversion to the

Negro appearance. Else why don't we seek segregation for our white "Tobacco Road" brethren?

In one sentence, you can sum up the average decent citizen in his working philosophy: "I'm all for giving colored people a fair break—I ain't prejudiced!—but don't ask *me* to go near them."

And that's precisely what our group *does* ask. Personal contact, on a friendly and social basis, is the best and quickest remedy on the market to wipe out that colored skin aversion or even awareness. I particularly recommend it for those just souls (and I feel sorry for them) who *want* to go all the way in their Christianity but just can't get their theology and their "feelings" to kiss and make up. Can these people, I wonder, take my word for it—for I wasn't reared, you know, with an exactly flaming affinity for my unknown colored sisters—that it's silly to regard this aversion as incurable?

It can be cured practically over the weekend: *if* you spend that weekend getting to know some Negroes as individual personalities, not just as a race to be helped or pitied or tolerated. Even when, with your will, you "love" the whole Negro race (meaning you don't damn them to hell), I still don't think it's enough. I'm not exactly saying that Saint Peter will bar your entry into heaven but neither do I think that the Lord in person will dust off a special chair for you. Those special chairs, they tell me, are for the generous souls.

And as for all the *inevitable* questions and fears and doubts and worries that arise whenever the Negro "problem" comes up, I have only this to say: when it comes to justice, we must do the hard right over the easy wrong and—let the chips fall where they may. Surely the Holy Ghost ought to be able to handle the chips.

As I say, I feel sorry for those Christians who bemoan

their prejudice and beat their bosoms in self-reproach, but
I also say—in the same breath—that God helps those who
help themselves.

What I'm also saying, still in that same breath, is that our
group, in its beguiling rather than bludgeoning way, affords
people this chance to help themselves. From the very beginning we have invited guests right and left to our meetings
and these guests have included the curious, the violently
prejudiced, the enthusiastic, the skeptical, and those who are
just blank on the subject. And how do we break down any
stiffness and resistance? The great common denominator:
FOOD. All God's chillun may not have shoes but they've
all got stomachs. And to get prejudiced souls eating with
colored people, elbow to elbow in a private home, is to chalk
up a rather significant victory. Once the horrible deed has
been committed, with no erasing the stigma, the Superior
Whites don't seem to mind their lowered estate one bit! In
fact, first thing you know, they're eating and chatting away
at a great clip.

But wouldn't a plate of tasty soda crackers, instead of the
array we set forth, serve just as well? I doubt it. We got
off on this lavish plane because the colored members—all
excellent cooks, several of them professional cateresses—
seemed to enjoy displaying their skill and heaven knows we
enjoyed eating it. We soon discovered that this talent for
beautiful food also had an apostolic value because, for one
thing, the party atmosphere puts everything on a social basis.
Not a social *worker* basis. And we settle qualms about
gluttony by telling ourselves: "If breaking bread together is
man's earliest symbol of shared equality and friendship,
why not pile our plates *high* while we're about it?"

Shifting from stomachs to hearts, I would like, in conclusion, to answer a question that I hope is simmering in the subconscious of at least a few readers: "Wonder if a group like this would work in *my* community?"

All I can say is that more good inspirations are snuffed out by too much caution—that unholy caution, I mean, that leaves *nothing* to Divine Providence—than this world dreams of. The only reason I hesitate to offer the gilt-edged guarantee of success to others is that I suspect that our group was singularly blessed, right from the start. It rather looks as if God had made smooth our path in a very particular fashion; as if He, knowing how easily we could fall flat on our faces, didn't quite dare to give us the usual rough testing of the spirit.

One is tempted to conclude, therefore, that this must have been a project dear to His heart. Isn't that enough for you to go on?

The Name Is Susan

THE AIRLINE hostess had bright blue eyes, bright honey-colored hair, and a bright and flashing smile. As if this were not enough in itself (for beauty is its own excuse for being) she was also a seasoned public speaker. I could tell she was seasoned because her opening line, and all speakers strive for an arresting opening line, almost made me quit breathing: "We are now flying, at an altitude of 8000 feet, over the Allegheny mountains."

Feeling as I do about flying, especially on a dark stormy night such as this was, I could have managed very nicely without this unpleasant reminder of my status quo. Couldn't she see I was trying to escape reality by burying myself in *The Case of the Careless Kitten?*

"Your pilot's name is Herbert Mitchell," she continued. "My name is Christine Fleming. We hope your flight will be a pleasant one. If there is anything I can do to make you more comfortable, please feel free to ask me. Thank you." And then, with another of those bright and flashing smiles, she turned to the passenger in the front seat. "Chewing gum, sir?"

Although Christine's speech seemed to lack a certain spontaneity, as well it might after the first four hundred renditions, it left me with a rather choked up feeling. It was pretty wonderful to realize that both Christine and Herbert, even though they'd never laid eyes on me before, were so anxious that I enjoy my flight. It is true that Herbert was too busy at the controls (and I most certainly wanted him to *stay* busy at the controls) to come in and tell me so in person, but this was a minor disappointment. The big thing was that both Christine and Herbert wanted me to be comfortable. They wanted me to be happy. They *cared*.

As the lovely Christine advanced down the aisle with the box of chewing gum in her hand, I couldn't help thinking of another great figure in history: Florence Nightingale, with a lamp in hand, comforting and sustaining *her* charges. Were not the chewing gum and the lamp but different symbols of the outstretched hand of mercy? Yes, here was another dedicated soul, I said to myself, who had chosen as her vocation to be a Friend to Man. Not in the Florence Nightingale setting (dim hospital wards) nor yet the Edgar Guest setting (in a house by the side of the road) but where a man *most* needs a friend. Eight thousand feet up in the air.

Small wonder, I said to myself, that my two grade school daughters—at an age when *I* had wanted to drive a Red Cross ambulance in France or donate my services to a leper colony —were forever writing English themes entitled: "Why I Want To Be An Airline Hostess." It is true that their themes seemed to stress the lure of foreign ports and the chance of meeting multi-millionaires and movie celebrities, rather than the humanitarian angle, but that would come with maturity. The point was that I had two Christines to give to

my country and, hence, was it not my motherly duty to prepare them for their vocations?

So I, sitting in the back seat of the plane as usual, asked
Christine—when she leaned over me with the chewing gum—
if she could, when she had a free moment, sit down and talk
with me.

She sat down immediately. "I'd adore it," she said warmly.

Somewhat abashed by all the warmth, I hastened to explain about my daughters. Since their present ideal was to
become airline hostesses, I told her, I would like to take
home some edifying little message. It might spur them on in
their academic pursuits, I said, if I were to tell them that a
hostess had to have a well-rounded education. Not just the
ability to pass out chewing gum.

Christine gave me her full and earnest cooperation. "Tell
your daughters," she said solemnly, "that one of the first
requisites is to be able to discuss any subject intelligently. I
mean, passengers appreciate it when we can carry on an
intelligent conversation about their own particular interests.
You know what I mean?"

The lovely Christine then proceeded to give me a practical
demonstration. She had, she said, chosen this particular
airline because any other shade of blue uniform simply
killed the color of her eyes, and a girl had an obligation, so
to speak, to bring out her best points. Did I know what she
meant? She didn't mean that looks were all that mattered
but just that a girl had an obligation, so to speak, to bring
out her best points. Did I know what she meant?

This thought-for-the-week exhausted (and it was pretty
heady fare for an altitude of 8000 feet), she next moved on
to the next topic she felt would be of most personal interest
to me. Namely, all the men in her life. This impressive

survey made me realize that I had grossly underestimated the lovely Christine. It seemed that she was not only a Friend to Man in the air, but on the land, and on the sea and, for all I knew, under the sea. I began to feel like Mary Worth, trying to untangle her love life, but I finally managed to narrow the field down to Ralph of Cincinnati and Freddie of Chicago. Freddie of Chicago, however, was obviously the superior man. Freddie had a yellow Buick convertible. Moreover, Freddie was not selfish about the yellow Buick convertible. Whenever she, Christine, had several days lay-over in Chicago, Freddie always handed her the car keys. "Here, Christy," Freddie always said. "The buggy's all yours." There was nothing quite so thrilling, said Christy, as zooming along Lake Shore Drive in a yellow Buick convertible. Did I know what she meant?

As we neared the Chicago airport, with Freddie no doubt lurking behind one of the hangars, I thanked Christy for having spent so much time with me. "Oh, that's perfectly all right," she said, with one of those flashing smiles. "Like I was telling you, that's part of our job. I mean, taking a personal interest in the passengers and being able to discuss all sorts of different subjects."

The next day, at the dinner table, I told my two daughters that I had had a long and interesting discussion with a real live airline hostess. She advised them, I said, to work hard in school and acquire a broad cultural background because one of the main requisites. . . .

"What'd you say her name was?" interrupted Susan.

"Christy," I said. "At least, that's what Freddie of Chicago —uh—I mean, some of her friends called her. But as I was saying, you have to have a well-rounded education and be able. . . ."

"Christy," repeated Susan, in a dreamy and far-away voice. "Gee, what a darling name. I suppose she spelled it with a C but I think a K would look even cuter, don't you?"

Two nights later, at the dinner table, my daughter announced that her official name, starting as of that very moment, was now Kristy Hasley. Would it be necessary to go to court or could she just change it herself? Anyhow, she had just passed her fourteenth birthday—was no longer a child —and her mind was definitely made up. Where would Judy Garland be today if she hadn't changed her name from plain old Frances Gumm? Or Robert Taylor if he hadn't changed his name from Arlington Spangler Bruges? (She had a good point there, with Robert, but I held my peace.) Moreover, there was no time to lose. She would be graduating from the eighth grade at Holy Cross in another two weeks and she most certainly wasn't starting her high school career under her present handicap. *Susan!* What had ever possessed us, she said with a shudder, to pick such a stupid and old-fashioned name as *Susan*?

Inwardly cursing the day I had ever met a fudge-brain named Christy (a Friend to Man indeed!), I tried to point out to Susan that I hadn't done too badly by her. How would she have liked, for example, to be called Utah? I once knew a family of Smiths, I said, who had named all their eight children after the states in the union. Arizona, Florida, Michigan, Utah. . . .

"You're not the least bit funny," she said coldly. "You're just treating me like a child. All I want to know is whether I can change the name myself or if I have to go to court. I'll bet Judge Pyle would listen to me."

That evening, after the dishes were finished, I got out Susan's baby book, covered with pale blue satin and sprinkled with painted forget-me-nots, to help my case. Hurriedly passing over the title page with its inscription of "Milestones on the rose-hued path that tiny toes must all too early leave behind," I came to the vital statistics page. There, under the heading of "From Dreams and Stardust and Hopes and Joys, our baby has arrived," I had written in a firm hand: "Susan Charlotte Hasley." Underneath, in an equally firm hand, was the doctor's signature: "Dr. David Bickel." That made the name of Susan, in the eyes of God and Society, pretty official and I sincerely doubted, I told her, if Judge Pyle would consider it a miscarriage of justice.

Moreover, did she fully realize what the name Susan meant? It meant "White Lily," and came from the Greek. Also, lucky girl that she was, her April birthstone was the diamond, signifying innocence. And did she realize that "Tuesday's child is full of grace?"

All in all, I pointed out, her name of Susan—plus all the other details of her birth—signified that she was an innocent white lily, full of grace. What more could any red-blooded American girl ask for? The name of Kristy, on the other hand, sounded too much like Crisco. Good for piecrusts but . . .

The white lily held her ground. "My name is Kristy!" she cried, with all the passion of Barbara Frietchie defending the stars and stripes. "You can't stop me! I have my own life to lead!"

There was more in this I-have-my-own-life-to-lead vein, and anyone with a fourteen-year-old daughter knows what I mean, but my husband and I exchanged patient and long-suffering looks. Why play the heavy-handed parent? This nauseating

"Kristy" phase would evaporate overnight just like Susan's equally passionate determination, after seeing "David and Bathsheba," to let her hair grow down to her waist. No sooner had she invested in a mail-order bottle of miraculous hair tonic ($1.49 out of her own allowance) than she had seen another movie—this time featuring Elizabeth Taylor with a poodle haircut—and lost all interest in Bathsheba's flowing mane. She had also, and this was the one edifying feature, bitterly regretted the $1.49 investment—especially when she couldn't browbeat her sister into taking it off her hands at half-price.

I do not, on the whole, approve of the "Never never thwart your child" school of thought but, on the other hand, there is much to be said for the doctrine of "Live and learn, Sister." (On more or less unimportant issues, I mean.) And, in this particular instance, I felt comfortably certain that any single-handed attempt on her part to turn into a Kristy, after fourteen years of being a Susan, was technically impossible. Certainly, *I* wasn't going to cooperate.

Besides which, she would be leaving for Camp Eberhart as soon as school was out. Two weeks of a disciplined, character-building, and wholesome back to nature program would make her forget the whole silly business. I was even more reassured, as camp drew near, when my daughter made no protest whatsoever about the name tapes (bearing the stupid and old-fashioned name of Susan) that I sewed into her shirts and shorts.

So it was with a light heart that I went up to camp, at the end of the two weeks' session, to fetch Susan home. My only concern (as I trudged down the hill from the Lodge—and through Robin Hood's forest—and around the archery range—en route to Cabin 14) was my failure to have sent her a chopstick. In her one communication home, a hastily scribbled post card, she had asked that I immediately send her a chopstick and I, understandingly enough, had been stopped cold in my tracks. (As it turned out, she had wanted a "Chapstick," for her chapped lips, but how was I to guess? I could only wonder, mystified, if Camp Eberhart was going oriental on me; turning out young Madame Butterflies.)

Oriental or not, Cabin 14—when I finally reached it—was empty except for one girl, sitting forlornly on her rolled bedding, and the counselor in charge: a strapping young female known as Miss Don. Introducing myself to Miss Don, I inquired about my daughter's whereabouts. "Oh, Kristy?" she said. Why, Kristy had gone up to the Lodge to have a last Coke with the girls. Kristy had left word for me to join her up there.

I sank down on a nearby cot while Miss Don went on to say, pleasantly, that Kristy had done very well with her crawl stroke. "That's nice," I said faintly. "And how did—uh—*she* get along with the girls in the cabin?"

"Oh, she adjusted very well," said Miss Don briskly, "except that she spent most of her time with Lori and Candy. We would prefer that the girls not just stick to their special friends from home."

"But I never heard of a Lori or a Candy," I said. This was as bad as the chopstick. . . .

Miss Don gave me a funny look. "Lori and Candy and Kristy all graduated from the eighth grade at Holy Cross together," she said rather coldly. "It's certainly odd you wouldn't know her best friends."

I felt like saying there were times when I didn't even know my own flesh and blood, but this was no time for philosophical reflections. What I had to face up to was the dismaying truth that I—by just a few careless words over the dinner table—had started the whole miserable business. (A horrible example, in reverse, of what Father Keller means with his Christopher slogan: "*You* Can Change The World!") Had I not mentioned an airline hostess named Christy, three teen-agers in Cabin 14 would still be using the decent baptismal names selected by their parents. It didn't take too much brain work on my part to figure out that Laurine and Patricia, under "Kristy's" diabolical influence, had now turned into a "Lori" and a "Candy." And I could only hope that "Candy's" mother, in particular, would someday be able to forgive me.

I started to explain all this to the counselor and then I decided it just wasn't worth the effort. Besides, didn't they call her "Miss Don" when she was listed as Dorothy Ledbetter on the camp folder? As I wearily started to trudge back to the Lodge, via the archery range and Robin Hood's forest, it gave me a certain feeling of security to know that Louis, back at the car, would still be Louis.

As we finally exited from camp that afternoon—with Susan, alias Kristy, wildly waving farewells from the back seat—we also exited to cries of, "So long, Kristy! See you in church, Kristy!"

Little did I know, in that dark hour, that the next eight months would be even darker. I would learn, during those eight dark months, grimly to acknowledge that I had a daughter named Kristy—if a clerk called to say, for instance, that the Ship'n Shore blouses that Kristy Hasley had ordered were in—but I, personally, never threw in the sponge. If there was a personal call for a character named Kristy, I would say doggedly: "You mean Susan? Just a minute, please. SUSAN! Telephone."

Yet as St. Teresa says in her famous bookmark: "Let nothing disturb thee, nothing affright thee, all things are passing. . . ."

For even fourteen-year-old daughters eventually turn fifteen and have a mysterious way, known only to God, his angels, and his saints, of beginning to acquire a little horse sense. Not too much, mind you, but at least enough to give you the necessary strength to carry on. (For instance, I naturally had to get Susan's okay on this essay and I am happy to report that she, from the vantage point of fifteen, even thought it "quite amusing.") Anyhow, Susan has now been Susan for a whole year and while, of course, she may some day turn into a "Suzanne," I really think the worst is over. *Laudate Dominum, omnes Angeli ejus; laudate eum; omnes virtutes ejus. Alleluja.* Praise the Lord, all you angels of his: praise him, all his armies. Alleluia.

The Invisible Fleet

THE OTHER DAY, as I was thumbing through *Modern Screen*, it suddenly struck me that if my knowledge of the liturgy were as rich and varied as my knowledge of Hollywood, I would be one of the main props of the liturgical movement. The Benedictines would be flocking to my door, seeking points of clarification. The editors of *Worship* would be begging me to join their staff. My own Bishop would be . . .

But why go on in this wistful vein? The point remains that here I am, with a painfully amassed knowledge of Life in Beverly Hills, and my services go a-begging. No one asks me about Mario Lanza's latest diet. No one asks me the real story behind Lana Turner's secret heartbreak. No one *even* asks me if I think Judy Garland will find the bluebird of happiness with Sid Luft. All this, and more, is at my fingertips and no one asks me.

It sometimes makes a person wonder if it's all worthwhile: this spending thankless hours ploughing through movie magazines, and beating off waves of nausea in the process, in order to keep up with my teen-age daughters. But how *else* would I ever know what they're talking about? (Heaven knows I don't even know the time of day when it comes to, say, the latest Nat King Cole or Fire House Five Plus Two recordings. What with three radios and two phonographs in the house, generally all going simultaneously, today's music means no more to me than the pounding of the surf at Lake Michigan.) Yet I had to keep *some* point of contact with my own flesh and blood and I reasoned, in my innocence, that the movies would be the least painful way out. Besides which, I was getting pretty tired of little domestic scenes like the following:

Me (attempting to enter the conversation): "And who in the world is Zsa Zsa Gabor?"

Daughters (collapsing in each other's arms and screaming with mirth): "You never heard of Zsa Zsa Gabor? Oh, *Mother!*"

That "Oh, *Mother!*"—and I seem to be hearing it more and more frequently—always makes me feel as if I'd just arrived at Ellis Island, black shawl over my head, and badly in need of a few classes at night school. "Thees Zsa Zsa Gabor, she is famous citizen, yes? I not know her. Is bad. Is ver' bad. But I learn, I study hard, if you bring me ze Americain—what you call heem?—movie magazines."

Well, anyhow, I would like to report that I occasionally ferret out items of real interest as I pursue my Hollywood homework. For instance, *Modern Screen* has lately been running a series of articles entitled: "How The Stars Found Faith." These spiritual odysseys would, of course, drive any theologian stark raving mad but I have found them quite interesting. For instance, I never before realized the fascinating elasticity of the word "faith." The only thing that is not elastic, in these articles, is the standard opening statement: "I belong to no particular church, if *that's* what you mean by religion, but I have always had a feeling that there is a Someone or a Something—it really doesn't matter what you call it—that is above and beyond us. The important thing, I feel, is that the individual have faith in himself to overcome insecurity or an inferiority complex," et cetera.

Hence, it was quite refreshing to pick up a recent "faith" article written by Jane Powell. You've never heard of Jane Powell of MGM? Oh, *reader!* Are *you* ever stupid! Well, let me tell you that Jane Powell is a little blue-eyed blonde, aged twenty-three, with a lilting soprano voice, and is happily married to her one and only husband (at the present writing). She is also, apparently, one of the best liked and most respected characters in Hollywood. She also doesn't know if she's coming or going when it comes to theology. But the refreshing note is that Miss Powell is the first movie star, in this series, to talk—quaintly enough—as if "faith" centered on God, and as if it was rather important whether God was a Someone or a Something. Equally refreshing is her admission that she hasn't got it all figured out. "Religion is a difficult subject for me," writes little Jane. "That which so many people take for granted, I often do not understand."

But the main reason that I'd like to quote, at considerable length, from her article (an article that is simple, undistinguished, and even naïve) is that it's a very disarming and even quite *touching* exposé of one sort of non-Catholic mind at work. And its very artlessness, not to mention the abundance of good will, struck me as being a most eloquent appeal for understanding and charity on the part of Catholics. Especially those Catholics who, living in their own tight little Catholic circles, tend to forget that "There, but for the grace of God, go I." There, had their parents not baptized and reared them as Catholics, would *they* go: perhaps without a shred of doctrinal truth to their names.

Faith *is* a gift, not just a pretty phrase in the catechism, and our scorn and impatience should be reserved for those Catholics who scandalize the little ones: not the little ones themselves. For this, I feel strongly, is how we should think of, and treat, the majority of outsiders: not as heretics (they don't know enough theology to be heretics) but as little ones, as Babes in the Wood, and as—God willing—potential Catholics. It's psychologically important, I think, to have this term—*potential Catholics*—always imbedded in our subconscious because then we'll keep the gate open for them. I mean, we'll keep the path clear—the gate open—maybe even a lamp burning in the window—in case that outsider should ever wander down our street. Faith is a gift, as I said, but there's no sense in piling up handicaps for the Holy Ghost!

But let our little Babe in the Wood speak for herself:

"My own family, the family which I am starting," writes Jane, "is a divided one, you might say, yet we are not conscious of it. My husband, Geary Steffen, is a devout Catholic. My little boy, Geary, will be brought up as a Catholic and so will the baby I'm now expecting. There was no quarrel about this, not even a lengthy discussion. I reasoned that since I didn't have any particular religion, but rather an attitude toward life, why should I be selfish and deny my husband the satisfaction of having his children brought up in a manner that would give him peace of mind? It does not disturb me at all that they will be Catholics. It would disturb him if they were not. That's all there is to it."

(There generally is *lots* more to it, with the non-Catholic mind at work, but our little Jane appears to be a generous soul.)

"I am grateful to Geary for his understanding way with me and I know he appreciates I can only be as I am. Some mornings when he gets up at dawn for an early Mass I forget myself and shake my head sleepily as if to ask, 'How can you do it?' He laughs and always adds, 'I'll say a little prayer for you, anyway.' And after he leaves, I may lie awake and direct inward accusations. 'Maybe you just don't like to get up and go to church, that's what your whole philosophy amounts to,' I tell myself. And then I may very seriously go over the whole matter again. The answer is always the same. I cannot be a Catholic. I cannot be a Methodist. I cannot be a Buddhist. . . ."

(God's grace has a way of handling "cannots", as we know, but there's this about it. Just as faith is a gift from God, so also is our precious free will. And rather than see unconvinced but generous Jane join up, just to please her husband, let us rejoice that her generosity stops short—as it should—rather than that she forfeit her integrity.)

"I have some Catholic friends, and because my children will be Catholics, I was disturbed one evening when these friends held that, since Catholicism was the first Christian religion, it represented the only true path. Now, I used to go to many different Sunday Schools. I found I liked them all and was disturbed by only one thing—by any sermon or quotation which tended to indicate that only this or that church was the true one. This would always make me think of the people I had seen in other churches and fear for them. To this day I cannot bring myself to accept the thesis that *any* people are denied God, no matter how they seek Him."

(Jane, Jane, I'm right with you. Nothing makes *me* so hot under the collar as when the statement "Outside the Catholic Church there is no salvation" is not properly explained. It's *tricky* to explain—for we must insist that ours is the true church founded by Christ—but I frankly think that you and Pope Pius XII would get along famously on the subject of salvation. Listen to what he very recently re-emphasized: "That one may obtain eternal salvation, it is not always required that he be incorporated into the Church actually as a member, but it is necessary that at least he be united to her by desire and longing."

Nor does this desire need always to be explicit or clear to a person's mind. "God accepts also an implicit desire, so called because it is included in that good disposition of soul whereby a person wishes his will to be conformed to the will of God." Boiled down, this means that salvation depends on our doing the best we can according to our lights. *What* could be more reasonable? And the Church has never officially stated that *any* man—not even Judas—is a lost soul because, after all, who knows? A man could repent in the split second before death. (Only don't *count* on this sort of dramatic finale, please. A hardened soul, in that last split second, would more likely be yelling "Help! Doctor!") Anyhow, the only person that the Church condemns, in the hope of knocking the fear of the Lord into him, is the man who—*knowing* the Catholic Church to be the true one—decides to go his own sweet way. But now let's get back to you and your story, little Jane.)

"There is a man I have known for some time who used to try to convert me to Catholicism. In a number of talks we came to no conclusion more overwhelming than that I could not take any such step. He knew this when he left me. Shortly afterwards he sent me a beautiful rosary. I was deeply pleased. Whether I was right or wrong about my beliefs, the sending of this gift indicated that he considered them worthy ones. At least that is how I interpreted the gesture and I feel it was what he meant. By my thoughts I had pleased him; by his thoughts he had pleased me. I might not, to his way of looking at things, have proper faith but he wanted to show that he, at least, had faith in me."

(May we pause for three minutes of silent prayer, at this point, and thank God for Catholics like this? I mean, he sent her a rosary—whatever the hopes or motives behind it—instead of sending her a time bomb.)

"My evening prayer is usually the one everybody knows from childhood, 'Now I lay me down to sleep.' When I first learned this prayer I was under the delusion that Jesus Christ and God were one 'man.' Later on I learned they were 'different' men. And still later on (and comparatively recently at that), I finally understood them as they are defined in the Bible. It may be that these changes in identification which I had to keep making have had something to do with my present thinking. I am not sure. It was disturbing."

(Jane, poor soul, is now smack in the mystery of the Incarnation: one person in two natures. She's disturbed? Ha! Better minds than hers have been disturbed. But at least she *is* disturbed, and *is* thinking, and has the courage to discuss it in a movie magazine that is dedicated, primarily, to the love life of Liz Taylor, Lana Turner, and Flaming Rita.)

"What I am perhaps trying to do now," concludes little Jane, "is learning to know myself. If I do it—well, maybe I will get to know Him and I am sure that if he is the Good Mystery I sometimes feel He must be, He will forgive my doing it my own way."

I would now like the jury to adjourn and deliberate—solemnly, objectively—on the spiritual status of Miss Powell. You have heard the facts from the witness herself. She has been *told*, by her Catholic friends, that the Catholic Church is the one true Church. She has also, apparently, not been spared the stark and unexplained follow-up treatment: that there is no salvation outside this Church and no salvation means, of course, eternal hell.

Very well. In spite of all this, Miss Powell just shakes her head "No" and acts confused. What's holding her up? What *ails* her?

Ladies and gentlemen of the jury, it is in your hands. But before you pass judgment on this wayward creature, I—as an ex-Miss Powell myself—would like a final word before you adjourn.

Many militant Catholics, in presenting their faith, seem to concentrate solely on the matter of salvation: a word that, if you ask me, has little or no meaning in the world today. At best, it seems to have a certain mocking "Drop a nickel on the drum and be saved" connotation; or to elicit an embarrassed "Oh, heavens, do we have to go into *that*?" The fact that many parents don't even bother to baptize their children —although they're mighty careful to give them all their immunization "shots"—speaks for itself. The word "salvation" has lost its punch.

So, instead of retreating into the desert—sulking and mourning over the lost word "salvation"—why not meet the world on its own terms? "Peace of soul," for example, is an expression that will mean something to it, as witness the wild flocking to psychiatrists and the tremendous sale of books like *Seven Storey Mountain*. In brief, stress peace and love rather than fear, and this, in turn, might instill a *healthy* fear of the Lord. (The fear of the Lord is the beginning of wisdom.) And, instead of striking a dire note of "*Unless* you do such-and-such," what's wrong with striking a positive note of what's to be gained in happiness right here on earth? (Was not St. Catherine of Sienna moved to say that all the way to heaven *is* heaven?)

Anyhow, I think it is downright cruelty to dumb animals —dumb in the sense of being spiritually unawakened and uninformed—to use "salvation" as a Gestapo's billyclub over their heads. A billyclub stuns without convincing. Rather, I think that we—who are to testify to the Light—should make it appear *as* light: not just as a grim and necessary way to save our own skins. Doesn't even the word "light" suggest clarity, warmth, comfort, and even beauty? Yet so many militant Catholics (perhaps to show what stern stuff *they* are made of) seem to feel it a sign of weakness, of compromise, to make Catholicism seem attractive. Me, I think it is attractive.

Moreover, Christ himself bothered to woo his listeners— his was more the role of a Divine Pied Piper than a Divine Gestapo—and his sermon on the mount was one of the most masterful campaign speeches of all times. Definitely, he held forth great promises and, definitely, he made the spiritual life sound not only appealing but compelling. And not until he had repeatedly tried to win their love and confidence, with his assurances of "Fear not, it is I" and "My yoke is sweet," did he come through with the sterner conditions of "Unless you do such-and-such."

Now, it strikes me as quite significant that Miss Powell (about whom I know practically nothing and whom I am just using as a symbol) has only two things to say about Catholicism: that it means getting up and going to church when you'd rather stay in bed, and that Catholics feel that only Catholics are entitled to heaven. Perhaps she knows lots more about it, for all I know, but these two things are what have impressed her the most. She can't see the light for the over-hanging darkness.

Faith *is* a gift, as I've said a dozen times, but one can't help wondering—since our little Jane seems both generous and humble—if perhaps some Catholic, somewhere along the line, didn't frighten Miss Muffet away? Some Catholic who, in explaining his faith, might better have used the Eliza-beth Barrett Browning approach: "How do I love thee? Let me count the ways!" And who, when it came to explaining religious tolerance, might well have quoted Father Vann: "We betray the Church when we develop a sectarian intoler-ance—not the divine intolerance which will not allow the truth to be whittled down to accommodate error and evil, but the diabolic intolerance which will not admit that others, too, may know something of the truth, and love and be loved by God."

Anyhow, one can't help feeling that there will be a happy landing for the Miss Powells of this world: that their childish "Now I lay me down to sleep" prayers (along with their con-fusion as to the "different men" that constitute God) may well be as pleasing—if not as liturgical!—as the Divine Office. Charles Péguy, in his poem called *A Vision of Prayer*, has God the Father—after reviewing the lovely and official prayers of the faithful—say this:

"Now I see the invisible fleet. And it is made up of all the prayers which are not even said, the words that are not even spoken.

But I hear them. Those obscure impulses of the heart, the obscure and good impulses, the secret good impulses,

Which unconsciously soar up, which are born and uncon-sciously ascend toward me.

And he in whose breast they originate is not even aware of
    them.

He doesn't know about them, he is only the originator.

But I collect them, says God, and I count them and weigh
    them.

Because I am the secret judge."

And so, on second thought—you ladies and gentlemen of
the jury—perhaps your services won't be required, after all.
Perhaps it would just be safer to leave the decision in the
hands of the secret judge.

There Must Be an Easier Way

IT HAS long been a secret disappointment to me that I've never been approached for jury duty, a Gallup poll, a Kinsey report, or even one of those Man-on-the-Street questionnaires. Imagine my delight, therefore, when Miss Fanny Butcher—in her *Chicago Tribune* column—tossed the following provocative questions right into my lap.

"A poll which, to my knowledge, has never been taken," wrote Miss Butcher, "would question lecturers about their audiences, where they find the warmest welcome, where intelligent listeners draw from them their subtlest quips—like a magnet lifting the hairpins from tightly wound curls. Would they find their ideal audiences across footlights, under the glow of chandeliers in private clubs, across the desks of college students gathered for discussion? Or, is there something about all formal audiences that denaturalizes anyone?"

After brooding over these questions for several days, I realized that I had a very real obligation to step forward and make my report to Miss Butcher. I was not, it is true, what you might call a seasoned public speaker, but where in the world could you find one more sensitive? Where find another who descended into the Valley of the Shadow every time she faced a group of over five people? Where find another who could more swiftly and more completely become "denaturalized?" (I take it that this expression has nothing to do with losing one's citizenship rights; that it just means "to become somewhat less than human.")

Besides which, I was just as interested as Miss Butcher in this quest for the Holy Grail: that is, an ideal audience. Up until now my standards had been fairly low. In my estimation, any audience was an ideal audience that didn't demand a cash refund at the front door. Yet here was Miss Butcher suggesting that a *really* ideal audience could, like a magnet drawing out hairpins, extract subtle quips from even a wooden Indian.

Frankly, I felt the whole thing smacked of occult powers, and yet who was I to scoff? After all, they scoffed at Columbus when he said "Sail on! Sail on!" and look what *he* discovered. Discovering this ideal quip-extracting audience couldn't be much harder, when you stopped to think about it, than discovering a new continent.

Yet I can't help feeling that there are certain conditions which *no* audience, no matter how occult, could possibly rise above. Such as, for example, the women's group that I once faced in Michigan City. I had been lured up there by the highly agreeable proposition that I, as the guest of honor, wouldn't have to open my mouth: a proposition *so* appealing that I guess I didn't, at the time, carefully listen to the rest of it. As it later dawned on me, what they wanted was the privilege of looking at me, while a panel of six women discussed me and my essays.

This bizarre arrangement became even more bizarre when, at the threshold of the Purdue Club, I discovered that my appearance was to come as a "delightful surprise" to the club members. Including, you understand, the six unsuspecting ladies on the panel. *They* evinced their delight, upon meeting me in the flesh, by just repeating "Oh, no—*no!*" in stricken accents. Only an obscure sense of club loyalty kept them, I'm sure, from bolting out the front door of the Purdue Club in a body.

One timid soul, in particular, looked as if she were going to be actively ill as we all filed in, Indian style, and took our places at a long discussion table. I, of course, sat in the middle and there I continued to sit—as impassive and inscrutable as Buddha—throughout the whole torturous performance. In one sense, I never had it so good before—for generally *I'm* the one that does the sweating—but it was still pretty uncomfortable. For one thing, it was quite awkward not knowing whether I should laugh appreciatively—or not laugh appreciatively—at my own witty remarks, as quoted by the panel ladies. I finally decided it would be better taste just to be Buddha. It was impossible, naturally, to play the role to the hilt—that is, contemplate my navel in true Oriental fashion —but I did spend the time inspecting my finger nails.

After it was over, the ladies presented me—for my afternoon's modeling services—with a huge bouquet of gladioli (from off the tea table), along with (and don't ask me *why*) two large boxes of Girl Scout cookies. Barely able to peer over the top of these offerings, it was extremely awkward trying to feel my way, by footwork, up the steps of the train and yet I couldn't help feeling that it was, all in all, an experience to be treasured.

So much for Michigan City. It stands alone in its uniqueness. In all my other ports of call, the audiences have been in fine fettle—relaxed, poised, in full possession of all their faculties—while I have been the denaturalized party. (Indeed, an audience in Milwaukee burst into loud laughter *before* I finished the joke I was telling and, for a minute, panic swept over me. Had my hat slid over one ear? A stocking fallen down? "Well, thank you for laughing," I said, uncertainly, "but would you *mind* waiting for the punch line?")

I would like to point out to Miss Butcher, however, that a speaker is often denaturalized, not to mention demoralized, before even reaching the platform. Sometimes, indeed, it takes only a small declarative sentence to undermine a speaker's aplomb. Such as, for example, the lady in Kalamazoo who rushed up to me just as I was walking into the auditorium at Nazareth College. "Are you *really* Lucile Hasley?" she cried out in a loud voice. "But I thought you'd be taller and have a more aristocratic nose!" The genuine distress in her voice left me shaken to the roots, even though I later received a note of apology. She assured me, in one of the smoothest recoveries of all time, that what must have seemed rudeness was really a marvellous tribute to my writing. That is, she had so identified herself with me—so graphic was I —that she was just *sure* I'd be tall and have an aristocratic nose like herself.

And then there was the lady in Chicago who, after what *I* considered the most magnificent speech of my career, wrote me the following note: "I am a professional book reviewer— in fact, I give dramatic readings—and I hope you won't mind my suggestion. Since I am taller than you are, and considerably bolder in self-assertion, why don't you just stick to your writing, dear, and let *me* present your material to the public?"

This came as a terrible blow because, as I say, my speech at the Morrison Hotel had been nothing short of magnificent. (Correction: Since I have only one speech in my repertoire, I should perhaps say I gave it my most magnificent rendition.) I don't say that the audience exactly leaped to their feet and screamed for more but that, *under the circumstances,* I had —like the little Judy Garland trooper I am—overcome great odds.

For one thing, I was—simultaneously—running a low-grade fever and having goosepimples. The goosepimples were due to the fact that I would, for the first time in my life, be speaking before a real live Bishop. And whereas Bishop Cousins was not in my own diocese, I figured that he might very well get in touch with *my* Bishop and start excommunication proceedings. Naturally, I didn't *intend* to be heretical but I have discovered—since lining up with the Catholic Church —that it's easier to run into heresy than to catch a common head cold.

My low-degree fever, on the other hand, was due to a three-inch wound on the left shinbone that I'd received, honorably enough, while pursuing the duties of my state of life. The night before, I had been out in the backyard trying to run down my small son, in order to give him a bath, and I had— in the gloaming—fallen on a rusty iron spike in the zinnia bed. A tetanus shot was advisable, said the doctor, as he bandaged me from ankle to knee, but it might also make me violently ill for Chicago. A delay of twenty-four hours, he felt, would not be *too* risky.

"Okay, I'll take the chance," I said, "but tell me what to watch out for. I mean, what are the first symptoms of lockjaw?"

The doctor shuddered. "Oh, I couldn't bear to describe them to anyone," he said.

As if this were not enough in itself (that is, having my leg swathed in bandages and expecting lockjaw to set in at any given minute), I had also had a strenuous experience going in to Chicago on the New York Central. The man in front of me—one of those Men of Distinction who had hoisted one too many—had given me his undivided, and even loving, attention. I would, at my age, have been enormously flattered except that the Man of Distinction (who was well on his way to becoming a Man of Extinction) could barely raise his eyelids.

"Lady," he kept saying, in a dreamy voice, "you've got something. I don't know what it is, Lady, but you sure got it." ("Lockjaw and stage fright, that's what I've got," I felt like telling him, but there was no point in encouraging the fellow.) This dreamy one-sided conversation, of course, quite charmed my fellow passengers, but they were beside themselves with delight when the Man of Distinction suddenly thrust his arm out at me.

"You know anything about materials, Lady?" he asked.

"No," I said, sulkily.

"Well, just feel my sleeve, Lady," he begged. "Best gabardine that money can buy. Go on, Lady. *Feel it*!"

By the time I reached Chicago, I was well on my way to a stage of complete denaturalization. Nor did the committee ladies, who gave me my last-minute directions before going on to face the Bishop, help matters any. Prior to this time, I had never bothered with any sort of formal salutation. I'd always stepped up to the microphone and said simply (and hopefully): "Friends."

Now, it appeared, I had to run through the entire Catholic litany.

"Say 'Thank you, Madame Chairman' and smile in her direction," they instructed me. "Then bow and smile at the Bishop and say, 'Your Excellency.' Then smile, but don't bow, and say, 'Monsignor Kelly.' Then say, but you don't necessarily have to smile when you say it, 'Reverend Fathers.' Then swing around to the audience again and say, 'Ladies and Gentlemen.' "

Small wonder that I, as I went through my Catholic paces, failed to notice the glass of water on the lectern. As I struck my hand against it, and felt the cold soothing water splashing over me and my typewritten notes, I reflected that one does, in a sense, go from one baptism to another. It somehow gave me the courage to shake myself off and proceed to deliver (no matter *what* that woman in the audience wrote me to the contrary) the most magnificent speech of my career.

Only I can't help feeling there's something sinister—even lethal—about Bishops. It was in front of my next Bishop— this time in Kansas City, Missouri—that I underwent my baptism by blood. I am not, please understand, being whimsical. I mean *blood*. Good red human blood. The stuff that hospitals charge you twenty-five dollars a pint for in giving transfusions. Moreover, I was in no condition, after my grueling attempts even to *reach* Kansas City, to spare even a drop.

To begin with, I was stranded for six hours at the Chicago Airport. You know the Chicago Airport? It is a large lovely madhouse, covering several acres, where people shake plane reservations under the noses of the desk officials and plead and scream for simple justice.

"Look," I screamed, waving my reservation under one of the noses. "Here am I and out there's my plane. *Why* can't I get on?"

"Because," said the man, "you were late."

"But is it my fault that the plane from South Bend was late?" I cried, still under the delusion that there *is* such a thing as justice. "Look, I got to give a speech in Kansas City at six o'clock."

"Yeah?" said the man. "Look, Lady, you go out and sit in the waiting room. Come back in an hour and try it again."

I went out in the waiting room and sat there, watching some cowboys on television, while two small children—en route to Japan—played ball with an empty coke bottle over my head. When it finally crashed at my feet, the mother turned to me. "They're restless," she explained.

Feeling somewhat restless myself by now, I went into a phone booth and put in a call to Kansas City. "Look, Sister," I said, "I'm stuck in Chicago. I'll never make it. You'd better start hunting up another speaker to take my place."

"Now, don't you worry, dear," came the soothing voice of this Sister Christine. "Everything's going to be all right. I'm starting right this minute to say my rosary for you."

"Oh, yeah?" I started to say, in the cynical tones of the airport official, but I caught myself just in time. As a stranded pilgrim, this was no time to deny the efficacy of prayer . . .

At precisely six-thirty o'clock, I fought my way onto a plane, en route to a six o'clock banquet in Missouri. I wasn't the least bit sure that my audience would still be waiting for me but, just the same, as I winged into the darkness, I began to worry about my "Fools Rush In" speech. Kansas City was just a *little* too close to the Mason and Dixon line for my own peace of mind. Would it, or would it not, be sheer suicide for me to include my usual little homily on racial prejudice—tell them about my own personal Negro friends?

As Providence would have it, the man across the aisle from me was wearing a Roman collar. Divine Providence, I thought to myself, has sent me this Man of God: to buoy me up with a pep talk to go forth and sow seeds, whate'er the odds. . . .

I leaned across the aisle and explained, in a low voice, my problem. "If you know what's good for you," whispered the Man of God, "you won't talk about Negroes in Kansas City."

"Then isn't that just the place," I whispered back, "where you . . ."

"Pardon me," said the lady I was sitting with, in a cool Protestant voice, "but would *you two* like to sit together?"

"No, thank you," I said in a cool Catholic voice. What might that emphatic "*you two*" mean? You two Papists? You two lovebirds? Anyhow, I figured I had troubles enough, at that point, without risking any raised eyebrows—starting any gossip about Men of God on airplanes. . . .

It was nine o'clock when I—like a last-minute landing of the U. S. Marines—dashed into the private club where Bishop O'Hara and a glittering assembly were waiting for me. I say "glittering assembly" because I could, even by the flickering candlelight, see that the women were dressed to the teeth and that, among the men, there was an occasional gleaming shirt front. I, on the other hand, in my wrinkled suit, looked like someone straight off a *Catholic Worker* soup line. It was perfectly marvellous for my humility, of course, but I couldn't help sending a wistful glance toward my suitcase. In my suitcase, parked at the door, was the attractive black crepe dress, with a draped skirt and jeweled neck clip, that Kansas City would never see.

As I looked over the glittering assembly, I had a sinking feeling—be it rash judgment or not—that they would probably just as soon shoot a Negro as say "Hello" to him. Hence, did it not follow that they would just as soon shoot a speaker who. . . .

"Friends," I began, with no conviction whatsoever that we would end on this note, "I am very happy this evening. . . ."

Despite my happiness, I became so nervous, as I neared the danger zone in my talk, that I started to untwist and fiddle with the paper clip from off my notes. Not realizing my own strength when it came to paper clips, I fiddled so vigorously that it suddenly snapped in two. Feeling a sharp prick, followed by something warm and sticky, I glanced down and discovered that the warm stickiness—"No," I thought to myself, "this can't possibly be happening to me." But it was.

It seems that I had, in one of the neatest tricks of the year, punctured a blood vessel and not just a teeny old vessel, mind you, but a veritable gusher. Instinctively, if somewhat wildly, I stuck my hand under the table and tried to wipe it off on the white linen tablecloth. The flow continuing, I next tried to *wrap* my hand in the tablecloth—in a sort of homemade tourniquet—and what Bishop O'Hara thought I was trying to do, God only knows. Maybe, for all I know, he figured I was just eccentric—*liked* to wrap myself up in tablecloths. . . .

Anyway, it was at this point that I decided to skip the cause of the Negro. Enough was enough. I'd had a hard day. In fact, it might be smart to sit down before I fell down.

I emerged from under the table and held up my bloody hand. "I'm sorry," I said, politely, "but I think I'm quietly bleeding to death up here."

Well, there *was* a doctor in the house and between him and the Bishop, with His Excellency himself applying the iodine, I got bandaged up. This touching but unscheduled scene took place, of course, in front of the entire audience, and a more heartless crew I have never seen.

At any rate, *here* was an audience that wasn't inhibited or denaturalized. I had, in the early part of the talk, jokingly

mentioned the woman who had requested my bones for relics
(in the happy event of an airplane crash) and now some
exuberant soul called out: "We don't want your bones in
Kansas City, Mrs. Hasley. Just your blood!"

Inspired by this sally, I held up the bloody tablecloth and
called back: "Well, now, here's a really first-class relic. What
am I bid?" And people, in presenting a book to be autographed, would come up with various lively variations of:
"We're not fussy in Kansas City. Just your X in blood will
be all right."

I wonder—was this what Miss Butcher meant by the "subtle
quip"? I wonder—was this bloodthirsty crew what she meant
by the ideal audience? If so, all I can say is that the price is
too high. I mean, *must* a speaker—in order to put everyone in
good humor—puncture a blood vessel? Anyhow, it was after
my Kansas City ordeal by blood that I decided there *must*
be an easier way to make a living than by public speaking.
Such as deep-sea diving or painting flagpoles or testing out
parachutes or—well, you name it, Miss Butcher.

And How Are You Today?

CONSIDERING THAT South Bend won the national Community Human Relations Award of 1951, it would certainly be very unseemly, if not downright unhealthy, for me to come out *against* brotherhood. The city fathers would have me tarred, feathered, and run out of town before sundown.

Yet do you suppose there would be any harm, especially since we've got the award safely stashed away, in making just a slightly unbrotherly suggestion? My suggestion, simple to a degree, is to have people quit saying "How are you?" to each other. It is my considered judgment that the elimination of this insidious and treacherous greeting would ultimately improve human relations just about 65%.

The trouble with saying "How are you?" to one of your brethren is that he is likely to think you really want to know the answer. Whereupon, in about seven hundred words and with considerable relish, he proceeds to give you very full coverage. Since your casual how-are-you was merely a concession to tribal custom and was *not* based on a morbid and

141

avid interest in the actual functioning of his bodily organs, this sort of medical report is not always fully appreciated. Indeed, it may instill sentiments of impatience, boredom, irritation, frustration, and even mayhem in the breast of the one who has unwittingly posed the question. Especially if he's in a hurry to catch a bus or make a movie before the prices change.

Yet it is perhaps even more dangerous to say "How are you?" over the phone than in a face to face encounter on a street corner. The reason for this is that most people have a chair near their telephones. Settling down comfortably, as they light a cigarette and kick off their shoes, they can thus devote more time and thought and detail to the how-are-you query. Obviously, this can be very very bad when the other party (the stupid party who has stuck out his chin and inquired about the other party's health) happens to be calling from a pay telephone booth. Not only is it perilous to his well-being, for the oxygen becomes very thin in a closed booth after several hours, but—if it happens to be a long distance call—it can ruin a man financially.

There are moments, as I say, when this sort of thing not only strains the bonds of brotherly love but can be an actual Occasion of Sin. In this case, the sin can take the form of what the theologians call "morbid delectation." There can be a good deal of morbid delectation, you know, in just *dreaming* about choking the person at the other end of the line.

Occasionally you run across people who know the Christian and civilized answers to the how-are-you greeting, which is just a hang over from the Red Man's original "How!", but even the best of Christians can occasionally slip. Instead of coming through with the regulation answers of "Why just fine, thank you, and how are *you*?" or "Can't complain" or "Guess

I'll survive" or "Oh, pretty good for the shape I'm in," they're liable to warm up to the subject and really let you have it. One of the worst of misfortunes, and it could happen to anyone, is to make the mistake of saying "How are you?" to a man who has just come from a dental extraction. With the experience still very fresh in his mind, you can count not only on an unusually splendid and graphic report but even a survey of the gaping hole in his lower left jawbone. Maybe, if your luck holds, he will even display the molar, wrapped in Kleenex, that he's taking home to show the wife and children.

All this is not to say, of course, that I frown on the giving of comfort to an afflicted brother. All I'm saying is that the situation should be *controlled*. The expression "How are you?" should be reserved for special occasions: such as when a man has just had a major operation or is recovering from bubonic plague or has his leg up on a pulley. In which instance, you know what you're getting into and are *prepared* to donate the time (hospital visiting hours from two to four) to listening and occasionally making appropriate little clucks of sympathy. This is a corporal work of mercy and Mother Church has always encouraged corporal works of mercy.

It is the other sort of thing—the being trapped, all unawares, by an innocent salutation—that weakens the bonds of brotherly love. Let us, by way of illustration, look in on Mrs. Edith Guggleheim. Mrs. Edith Guggleheim is a very busy woman, what with her five small children, and yet she somehow manages to be the right-hand man of Father McKloskey.

It is a bright sunny morning. Mrs. Guggleheim, full of early morning apostolic fervor, decides to tackle her apostolic chore of the day. Father McKloskey, and we shall soon see what a smart operator *he* is, has asked her to notify the fifteen members of the St. Ambrose League that the evening's meeting has been changed from 7:30 to 8:15. Mrs. Guggleheim picks up the receiver and dials Liverwurst 7890, humming a gay little snatch from *Oklahoma!* as she waits for the connection: "Oh, what a beaut-i-ful morning. . . ."

Mrs. G.: "Harriet? This is Edith Guggleheim. How are you this morning?"

Harriet: "Oh, I can't say that I'm a bit well, Edith. I didn't sleep a solitary wink all night long and how I'm going to get through the day, I just wouldn't know. Honest, Edith, I'm as weak as a kitten."

Mrs. G.: "Oh, I *am* sorry, Harriet. I know how annoying it is to have a restless night. Well, look, Harriet, I'm just calling to say . . ."

Harriet (reproachfully): "Oh, it's not losing my sleep that's the trouble. I've put up with the worst sort of insomnia for years, my dear. I'm as weak as a kitten this morning because of my stomach, and you know my stomach. Or do you? As I was telling Henry this morning, no one really knows what I go through with my acid indigestion. Heaven knows I watch my diet like a hawk but, honestly, Edith, the *least* thing seems to curdle up on me. You'll never believe this, Edith, but all I ate last night was some fried cabbage—Henry's so fond of it, you know, fixed with sausage drippings—and a wedge of cheesecake and, honestly, Edith, you'd have thought I'd eaten rat poison. My stomach's just that delicate. Well, I had Henry get up around three o'clock this morning—no, wait, it was nearly four o'clock because I remember telling Henry that that's when so many hospital cases die. Four in the morning. You ever know that before, Edith? Well, anyway, Henry went down to the kitchen and fixed me some hot water with baking soda but, honestly, Edith, it hardly relieved me at all. Oh, it brings up some of the gas, of course, but it leaves you as weak as a kitten and as I was telling Henry . . ."

Twenty minutes later, Harriet—being weak as a kitten—finally comes to a full stop. Mrs. Guggleheim, however, is so gassed herself by now that she doesn't even realize Harriet *has* stopped.

Harriet: "Edith? You still there? I thought for a minute we'd been cut off. What was it you said you were calling about?"

Mrs. G. (faintly): "The St. Ambrose League—the meeting tonight—time changed from 7:30 to 8:15. . . ."

Harriet: "Oh, that. Well, I'll tell you, Edith. I just don't think I'll be able to come anyway. Henry and I were planning on driving out to Rosie's Ranch for dinner tonight—Henry's so fond of their barbecued spareribs, you know—and I'd never make it back in time. Thanks for calling, though, Edith. Mighty nice hearing from you."

Mrs. Edith Guggleheim, with fourteen more ladies of the St. Ambrose League yet to be called, totters over to the davenport and lies down. Outside, it is still a bright and sunny morning but Mrs. Guggleheim is no longer interested in the weather, the St. Ambrose League, her fellow men, or restoring all things in Christ. Mrs. Guggleheim knows, of course, that the apostolic life isn't *supposed* to be easy—did not St. Paul himself suffer prison, shipwreck, and forty lashes?—but Mrs. Guggleheim, for the nonce, is beyond comfort. All she can think about are the fourteen remaining calls to be made; the fourteen times she must pick up the receiver and say: "Hello, this is Edith Guggleheim. And how are *you* today?"

"*Feelings Don't Count*"

T HIS IS going to be the sort of essay that should, by all the laws of Holy Prudence, be one of those anonymous jobs. Good old anonymous! It offers one such cute little titles to hide behind: "Madame X"—"A Well-Wisher"—"Indignant Taxpayer"—"Reproachful Citizen"—"Militant Mamie"— "Occupant of the Sixth Row from the Front at the 8:30 Mass". . . .

Alluring as these titles are, I am—nevertheless—signing my own prosaic but real name to this bill of complaints. Not because I'm necessarily partial to red—a martyr's funeral *does* rate red, doesn't it? . . . or fancy myself as another Catherine of Sienna, bossing the Popes around, but because— well, because it seems that I'm a "natural" for the job at hand. *Someone* has to be the fall guy and I do have one very excellent qualification: no one, in his right mind, can possibly label me anti-clerical.

Rather, my name has become a sort of "I Like Priests" label to hundreds of readers (what Boston is to baked beans, Hasley is to Holy Orders!) for I've not been the least bit bashful in airing my sentiments. Heaven knows I didn't *plan* a career along this line but, by now, my lone claim to fame appears to be this: "Lucile Hasley? Oh, yes. Isn't that the South Bend dame who likes priests so much? The eccentric writer who claims that priests are her favorite people?"

And it's true. I, eccentric as all get out, know at least six priests for whom I would cheerfully chop off my right arm—if they really wanted my right arm—and another round dozen for whom I would lop off my left arm. I know this all sounds rather bloody (and I hope no cleric puts me to the acid test!) but you *do* get the general idea? I want it to be very very clear because I am prepared to shoot, on sight, anyone who dares to tamper with my cherished pro-clerical label.

Trusting that I have made smooth my path, I would now like to creep cautiously up on my objective: I would like to claim from you clerics a modest little fee for my press-agent services! I have a very real grievance to present and—will you priests give me a fair hearing? Will you at least *listen*?

What, I would like to ask, happens to some of you priests in the confessional? For this convert's money, the metamorphosis that sometimes takes place—from Shepherd to Scorpion—is the most disconcerting thing ever to come my way. I like priests—yea!—but that liking has occasionally taken a fearful drubbing in the confessional. No penitent, they tell me, has yet been killed outright but you can, you know, slowly kill the intangibles: confidence, trust, liking, respect, and spiritual interest.

What, I wonder, is wrong? Has hearing confessions become a lost art? I strongly suspect that it's not lack of skill that's gumming up the works . . . nor the priest's stomach ulcers nor arthritis that's plaguing him . . . but an *unawareness*, on the priest's part, of the importance of confession to the laity. I can't quite believe that absolution is the *only* objective but, if it is, don't tell me! I prefer to believe the spiritual books and hang on to a few dreams.

Seriously, do you priests really want the devotional or "tonic" confession to wither and die on the vine?

Do you think it's your sermons and Catholic Action meetings that are the Big Influence and that confession—the *only* personal contact for most parishioners, especially in our modern over-sized parishes—is very incidental?

Do you realize that most people judge a priest more on his performance as a confessor than by his public utterances and Good Works all rolled together? ("This is the sort of priest he really is, when no one else is around to listen.")

Do you perhaps count *too* heavily on the standard dogma: "Priests are only human. You hafta consider human nature. And human nature and 'feelings' don't count. It's the automatic operation of the Sacrament that counts, not the human operator. It's about time the laity got that through their thick skulls."

Okay. Feelings don't count. (Who am I to bang *my* thick head against the theologians and philosophers?) *But of what profit, you priests, to be theologically correct and, in practice, scare off and lose your untheological sheep*? Our skulls are often *very* thick, but there's one universal language that we can grasp: kindness. Feelings, I'm afraid, are here to stay.

But, if you want to operate on just sheer logic, why not let it work both ways? Where, for instance, is the logic in bulldozing a penitent who says he is doubtful about something? Doubtful means doubtful, doesn't it? And where is the logic in jumping to fantastic conclusions? Such as the time I once mentioned "impatience toward my children" and the priest thundered back: "And why, Madame, aren't your children baptized?" (A non sequitur that I'm still trying to figure out.

I sometimes have the eerie feeling that the priest is still lecturing the penitent who has just left and hence I always feel sorry for the penitent who follows *me*. Will he bear the brunt of *my* sins?)

Incidentally, I would like to say that when this gripe job of mine first appeared in *The Priest* magazine, I received—naturally—a goodly number of communications from the priest readers. Ninety-nine percent of them were exceedingly good-natured about the whole thing—this being publicly spanked by not only a convert but a *female*—and good-naturedly pointed out their side of the picture. One priest pathetically pointed out that he was over six feet tall and that the architect, in designing that particular confessional, apparently had a midget in mind. It was rather rough, he said, to have an angelic disposition when you were doubled up like Houdini in a strongbox. Another priest pointed out that—when it came to kindness—why didn't the laity chew Sen-Sen to remove the onion and garlic breaths? Spiritual direction, he said, was rather difficult when you were being slowly asphyxiated.

One priest, however, came through with a letter that perfectly illustrated my point. That is, his batting average was 100% when it came to *missing* the point. "Mrs. Hasley's troubles in the confessional," he wrote the editor, "could have been settled by just a simple clear-cut answer of "Yes" or "No." *Were* her children baptized or not?"

(Public announcement to all who are interested: Mrs. Hasley's three children *are* baptized.)

Yet those clerical responses, on the whole, perfectly illustrate another point—and one of great importance. It's only the *occasional* priest who turns into a Scorpion in the confessional and who can well afford a little examination of conscience. I want to make this clear because, as I write this, I am painfully aware that "outsiders" aren't going to be too edified by this outburst. Yet any outsider with a grain of common sense should realize that the Church Militant is not composed of bona fide saints. They're just *trying* to reach that status! And it might actually be edifying for outsiders to realize that we, the laity, are not "crushed and downtrodden peasants." The very fact that this little diatribe of mine is being published, under Catholic auspices, should make Paul Blanshard—in his claim that Catholics aren't permitted to think for themselves or "speak up"—look somewhat foolish.

And now, let's get on with my diatribe.

Feelings don't count in the confessional? Okay. But it's somewhat like the old wheeze: "The operation was successful but the patient died." The absolution was valid but the penitent lost all interest in the spiritual life, right then and there. The absolution was valid but the penitent, mortally wounded by the gun-fire, crept away muttering: "Never again!"

Even when one *knows* the correct theological responses to bitter confessional experiences ("This obviously happened for my own spiritual good!"—"One shouldn't seek consolations!"—"It's very beneficial to operate on just Sheer Faith!" —"If I intended a good confession, it *was* a good confession!"), it seems to me that only a St. Thérèse could *thrive* on such a diet. For the rest of us, prone to feelings as we are, it might well leave us with spiritual rickets.

What you priests don't seem to realize—for the main and simple reason that people don't go around discussing their confessions—is that 98% of your power, for good or bad, lies in that little box of yours. I'm not expecting you all to be replicas of the Curé d'Ars but—man alive! just a *little* kindness and courtesy go so very far. Even if you're bored into a stupor on your side of the fence, it does seem that you might—as a bare minimum—toss in a few "tricks of the trade": such as a simple "God bless you" or "Go in peace" or "Let us now thank God for this good confession." (And that whispered "Say a prayer for me, will you?" from a priest makes the layman feel wonderful. Sort of proud and touched that his prayers are worth a little something, maybe.) There's also the little liturgical touch that's quite nice ("Next Thursday is the feast of Corpus Christi and so let us, during this coming week, remember," et cetera) but, actually, it doesn't too much matter *what* touch is used. All I ask, pathetically, is *something* that smacks of the spiritual, something to make it seem like a sacrament rather than a mere chore.

Feelings don't matter, of course, but there's nothing like breaking your neck to get to confession, standing patiently in line, throwing your soul into a good confession and then getting only: "Three Hail Marys," in a voice midway between a grunt and a groan, and—wham!—goes the slide in your face.

Is the Sacrament of Penance what the spiritual books claim or is it just on a par with brushing your teeth or having a quick gargle?

We laymen regret, naturally, that our confessions aren't more entertaining. But can *we* help it if we're neither in the unitive way nor hardened fugitives from a Georgia chain-gang? We're mostly average citizens with ordinary boring sins, *but* you priests might—through confession—keep lifting us from notch to notch. That calloused soul might become lukewarm; the lukewarm catch on fire; the "on fire" be inspired to "spread fire." Even that pesky scrupulous soul ("Bless me, Father, I accidentally sat down on a prayer book") might, with wise and gentle handling, pass into the "tender" soul stage. And, most important of all, the troubled but timid souls—as they gain confidence in you—might advance past the "I forgot my morning prayers on two occasions" and *really* reveal what's on their minds.

Too much bother? Not enough time? Line waiting? Well, my doctor always has a packed waiting room. No matter when your appointment, you can count on sitting for hours—indeed, I've often toyed with the idea of bringing along my lunch in a shoebox—but, once you make the inner sanctum, you really get your money's worth. Perhaps it's because doctors are realizing, more and more, that a quick prescription of bicarbonate of soda isn't the answer to a stomach ache. Maybe your mother-in-law is living with you?

Anyhow, the best confessor I ever had in my life once said to me (when I timidly mentioned there was a line waiting): "At this precise moment, you are the only person in this church who matters." And that, to me, sums up the very essence of the confessor par excellence.

If this essay were just a case of licking my own wounds, it wouldn't have much value. I have wounds to lick, all right, but that's not the point. *I'm* all right. *I'm* one of the lucky ones for I have a bulwark of four-star priests in my background. (And can lift my eyes to that star-studded firmament whenever my spirit fainteth.) Moreover, I have a wonderful outside spiritual director to pick me up and bind my injuries whenever I'm wounded in battle. (The battle, you understand, is trying to find a good available confessor among the harassed parish priests: a project somewhat like trying to find uranium in your backyard.)

Yet even when you have a spot of luck, you can't count on finding the same man next time. The name over the confessional may be "Father McGillicuddy" but—and this is a dirty trick—his assistant, Father Scorpion, may be occupying his box instead. Like Pandora, you don't know *what* you're going to find.

But, as I was saying, I'm not writing for myself. Honest. I'm speaking up on behalf of my more inarticulate fellow laymen and—believe me!—I know whereof I speak. Ever since I started writing Catholic essays, I have been swamped by letters from all over the place—mainly from priests and converts. (The priests, to a man, cheer me on: thus making me feel like a stinker as I compose *this* little job.) It's the converts, though, who weigh heavily on my soul. They're *such* tender blades of new grass that they don't thrive very well under the Iron Heel and I find myself a very busy ministering angel indeed. Smarting from my own wounds, I doggedly keep writing back to my convert correspondents: "FEELINGS DON'T COUNT."

Are these sensitive souls too ultra-*ultra* sensitive? I used to think so, back in the days when I was having such smooth sailing, but now I no longer can brush them off.

May I, please, cite one of my recent rough experiences? (Incidentally, I sometimes wonder if Divine Providence *sent* me this rough stretch in order to provoke a necessary essay? But no, that sounds as if I were Michael the Archangel in person. Frankly, I think I brought the "rough stretch" on myself because I *did*, several years ago, come down with an elegant case of scruples. And the nervous scrupulous person, let me tell you, is enough to try the patience of a saint. Anyhow, the experience left me in a rather weakened condition—I no longer faced confession with the old aplomb—and my voice, in spite of myself, would get rather shaky.) Well, on this particular day, I crept into the confessional with a very routine and pared-to-the-bone confession and—thanks to the excellent and patient coaching of my outside spiritual direc-

tor—managed to get through a letter-perfect performance.
(The time before I'd inadvertently used the word "several"
in reference to a venial sin and been shot down in mid-air.)
But, unfortunately, I guess my voice must have trembled a
little from the strain. Roared my man: "All right now, come
clean! You wouldn't be this nervous if you weren't concealing
something. Cut the stalling and tell the truth!"

Feelings don't count? Thank God, they really *don't* count—
metaphysically speaking—but, please God, let our faith survive and surmount these unmetaphysical feelings of ours!

I emerged shaking like an aspen leaf and wept for ten
minutes in a back pew, fervently hoping that all bystanders
would think it a sudden attack of hay fever. I also admit that
my tears were tears of pure unadulterated anger and indigna-
tion. All I could think, shocked to my toes, was: "Dear God!
A priest like that could damage you for life. What would *I* do
if I didn't have my 'other kind of priest' to revive me?"

And that, in a nutshell, is why I feel so vehemently about
all this. Knowing how good confessors *do* operate, and in-
debted for life to them for their marvellous direction, I find
it mighty hard to lower my standards. It is also very hard—
when you love the Church intensely—not to *care* what goes
on. And, as far as I can figure out, the only alternatives to not
caring are to become either hard-boiled, or utterly apathetic,
or treat it all as a big joke: none of which particularly appeals
to me. I prefer to be a member of the Church Militant instead
of the Church Insufferable.

By and large, we laymen are an inarticulate group—both
in confession and out—but do, please, give us the benefit of
the doubt as regards our good will and earnestness. A dopey
confession doesn't necessarily mean that a spiritual dope is
kneeling before you. Maybe not even the village idiot! Maybe

not even a cunning little shyster who is out "to put something over" on you priests and God!

What may be kneeling before you is a temporarily paralyzed soul. A soul who has a very real problem and who needs your help desperately but who—when the slide goes back and the priest growls "WELL, and when was YOUR last confession?"—quietly gives up the ghost.

Gather at the River

I FEEL THAT high school class reunions, if people *have* to have high school class reunions, should be managed along more humane lines. That is, I feel they should be held annually. Preferably semi-annually. Certainly, it's too great a shock to the nervous system to wait a *quarter of a century*, such as my class of '27 did, before gathering at the river.

I didn't know, of course, what Time and the River had done to my old South Bend Central chums but the last time they'd seen *me*—well, I'd been a petite, ukelele-playing, seventeen-year-old Presbyterian with spit curls. Since then, there'd been some changes made.

"What dress should I wear?" I asked my husband nervously, on the evening of June the twenty-first. "What makes me look most petite?"

"*Petite!*" he said, his jaw falling a good three inches. "Don't you think it's a little late in the day to be worrying about—look, dear, why don't you just have a stiff scotch-and-soda before you go?"

"The committee," I said, with simple dignity, "is taking care of *that*, thank you." Indeed, that was the one and only thing that the committee, on which I'd served, could agree upon. After twenty-five years, agreed the committee, only alcohol could make the whole thing bearable. Without a cocktail hour preceding the banquet, how could anyone—after getting a load of the lame and the blind and the halt—be able even to enjoy the food?

Aside from this crying need for liquid anesthesia, though, the committee couldn't seem to come to grips on much of anything. Someone suggested an evening of dancing and was hooted down, with cynical hoots, by the treasurer. The budget couldn't afford, he said, to have a crew of osteopaths on call, waiting in the Oliver Hotel lobby. It wouldn't be so bad, of course, if people would just stick to a slow waltz or maybe the minuet, but *some* fat-headed idiot would be sure—with nostalgic bravado—to call for the Charleston.

Wouldn't it be far better, and safer, just to set up some tables for Mah Jong? Or, how about putting on some funny skits? Maybe a style show featuring the felt helmets and gunny sack dresses we girls had worn back in '27?

No skit, said one of "we girls" glumly, would seem even *remotely* funny after we all got a good look at each other, circa 1952. Why not run off some colored films on, say, our National Parks? Or, maybe, have a lecture on Cancer Detection?

"Well, we'll work out the entertainment later," said the chairman. "Anyway, the questionnaires are coming in fine. Only one classmate, so far, is in the penitentiary and there's been only one suicide reported and—say, did anyone track down Charlie Plimhimmon? *I* heard he was dead but we don't want to print him on the obituary list, of course, until we're sure."

"What *is* the latest score on the dead?" I asked, nervously glancing around the table. Two, four, six, eight—well, none of the committee, at least, had died off since last week's meeting.

The chairman glanced down at his papers. "Well, let's see —with Charlie Plimhimmon, if he *is* dead, that is—well, it looks like twenty-eight."

There was a prayerful three minute silence, as was only proper, and then the chairman said, rather firmly: "I think we ought *definitely* to rule out any dancing, don't you? Just hire a string trio for some soft background music? I mean, there's bound to be a lot of people with high blood pressure and coronary conditions and I—well, as chairman, I'd like to keep the casualties down to twenty-eight."

Feeling like casualty #29 coming up, I slunk into the Oliver Hotel lobby on the evening of June the twenty-first. I was wearing, after much agonizing indecision, a neat black and white print that did nothing for me whatsoever except make me *feel* more like a chameleon; more like just background. In fact, the dress always reminded me of the experience a fortyish friend of mine—seeking a similar job of protective coloring—had had in one of the local dress shops. My friend had rejected every offering hauled out by the salesgirl, as being either too extreme, too young-looking, too bright, or too razzle-dazzle. As she left the store, the salesgirl had murmured politely: "Try us again some day, Madame. Some day when you're not looking for a *shroud*."

Anyway, here I was: slinking into the lobby, wearing my neat black and white shroud, and wishing I also had a Halloween mask. Over by the elevator, half-shrinking behind a potted palm, was another woman wearing a neat black and white print. Only she had a bolero jacket.

We eyed each other speculatively. "Aren't you Lucile," she began nervously, "I mean, that is, didn't you *used* to be Lucile Hardman? I remember you were on the volleyball team. I don't suppose," she continued in a wretched voice, "that you remember me?"

"Gee," I said, in an equally wretched voice, "you certainly look familiar but I—uh—were we on the volleyball team together? You're—wait a minute, now—you're Edith—no, wait—you're Ethel—"

"Gladys," she said mournfully. "Gladys Hannafeld. They used to call me "Glad." Only I wasn't ever on the volleyball team. I wasn't the athletic type like you were."

"Glad" and I stepped into the elevator together. I, personally, felt very bucked up—this being remembered as a past athlete—but I was afraid I hadn't done much for Glad's morale. "I'm married," Glad was saying, still in that wretched voice, "but I couldn't get my husband to come along."

"Me neither," I said, with true regret. (If only he could have heard, with his own ears, that reference to me being the athletic type!) "He hasn't yet recovered from *his* class reunion at Notre Dame two years ago. Heavens, you should've seen him when he came home, wearing the silliest little baseball cap. I'm certainly glad *our* reunion is going to be on the dignified side. I'm not sure what's on the program but I do know they decided to keep it sophisticated and dignified."

As we stepped out of the elevator, we were practically knocked down by one of the committee members rushing by, carrying two live rabbits by the ears. "Don't tell anyone," he hissed, getting a fresh grip on their ears, "but this is one of the prizes. You know, for the person having the most children."

"Well, anyway," I said to Glad, as we walked over to the registration desk, "I know for a fact we won't have to wear baseball caps."

As the woman at the desk handed me a little typewritten card, bearing my name, she said with a certain sharpness: "I remember *you* all right. You beat me in the croquet finals at Camp Tannadoonah."

My athletic prowess, by now, was beginning to embarrass me. To soothe old wounds, I assured her I probably couldn't sight a wicket three feet away by now and then proceeded, all unwittingly, to prove my point. "You've pinned your identification card on upside down," she said, pointing to my bosom. She looked, I thought, quite happy about it.

The general idea behind the typewritten cards, I'm sure, was that they would prove helpful in guessing who everyone was. Lacking a magnifying glass, or even bi-focals, I found it only added to my embarrassment. I mean, having to lean way over and peer at names—grazing my nose on brooch pins and buttons in the process—and then straightening up with a glad cry of: "But of course! Naturally I recognized you right off! I just wanted to check the *married* name!" (This couldn't work, obviously, with the men. With them, I cried: "But of course! I just wanted to see if you were a captain or colonel by now!")

My worst moment of the evening, when it came to peering at names and making a suitable comeback, was when I spelled out "Charlie Plimhimmon." I sprang back in alarm. Almost, but not quite, I'd screamed: "But you're supposed to be *dead*!" A greeting which, I'm sure, would have bucked Charlie up no end. Bucked up anyone.

The highlight of the evening—and a moment I'll always treasure—was when some unlabeled gentleman, about four and a half feet tall, came up and said in a husky voice: "Lucile, you won't remember me but I want you to know that I—well, I've never been able to forget you."

"You mean," I said suspiciously, "because I was so athletic? Because I was on the volleyball team?"

"*You? Volleyball?*" His pained look implied I was too ethereal even to bat a ping-pong ball. "Gee, no, Lucile, I always remember you as you were on Stunt Night—doing a tap dance and playing 'Five Foot Two, Eyes of Blue' on your ukelele. Since then, I've just never been able to forget you."

"Really?" I murmured, in a highly gratified voice. (What a *wonderful* evening this was, after all. The string trio, in the background, was playing a medley of "Whispering," "At Sundown," and "Sleepy Time Gal." And here was this faithful old admirer of mine, all four and one half feet of him, practically drooling at my feet.) "You mean," I went on, softly, "that you've never married?"

He had the grace to blush. Well, yes, he admitted, he *had* got married. Had four kids, in fact.

I rallied swiftly. "And is your wife here?" I asked, glancing around the vicinity for any likely midget.

"Oh, *she's* home painting the bedroom furniture," he said, with boyish simplicity. "Anyway, Lucile, I just wanted to tell you," and here his voice grew husky again, "that I always thought you were the prettiest girl in the whole class. In fact," and here his husky voice really scraped the bottom of the barrel, "you were always sort of my dream girl."

I lean, by nature, toward a healthy scepticism but, considering my friend's height, I didn't doubt his statement for a minute. I had always been so very short myself that I was always the dream girl of every runt in the class. While the other girls danced off with all the six foot athletes, I was always pursued—but madly—by all the male dwarfs.

Tonight, it seemed, was no exception. "And what do you do now, Lucile?" my little dwarf was saying, shyly.

It seemed cruel to mention that I had three children and a basket of unironed clothes awaiting me at home, after this mad and intoxicating evening was over, because I knew it would pain him as much as the volleyball. If *only* I could report that I had, in a command performance, played my ukelele before the crowned heads of Europe. . . .

"Well," I said, lamely, "I write things. I have a weekly magazine column and have had a book published and give out of town lectures and . . ."

"Lectures!" said my little dwarf with a terrified expression. "Book! Good Lord, what *about*?"

"Well," I said, "it was sort of a Catholic book. You see, I . . ."

But my little admirer had somehow vanished into the crowd. Maybe, for all I know, he suddenly felt the urge to call up his wife and check on the painting job.

But it was still a lovely evening. For dinner we had spring chicken, mashed potatoes, fresh peas, avocado salad, and peach melba. The string trio, in the background, played "Ramona"—"Always"—and "Little Coquette" as I listened to my dinner partner, a dentist from Cleveland, explain the effects of chlorine on dental decay. Someone got up and gave a speech about how we were the children of the Great Depression but how gamely we had, nevertheless, clung to our ideals and followed through. By way of proof, he introduced Marilee DeHaven. Marilee DeHaven, who back in school had

had long golden curls that hung to her waist, was introduced as now being a successful dance instructor in Hollywood. Whereupon Marilee—*still* with long golden curls that hung to her waist—kicked off her shoes and did a swooping ballet dance, among the tables, to "Tea For Two."

It just went to show, I thought to myself, as I gnawed my chicken, that there was no excuse for any woman—with any git up and go—not to keep in trim. Me, I couldn't even remember two chords on my old ukelele.

"And now," said the toastmaster, "I want each of you to write down, on the white cards you see by your plates, all the information you can dig out of the person on your right. Then Dan here—and you all remember *Dan*—is going around the room with a walkie-talkie and let each of you have a turn at the mike. Start digging, folks!"

I dug out, from the pretty and brown-eyed lady on my right, that she was now a local Christian Science reader. She, on her part—although she wasn't *supposed* to do any digging —observed pleasantly: "I hear *you're* a fallen-away Presbyterian. Is it true you went over to Rome?" This so startled me, for I'd never heard "fallen-away" used quite that way before, that I almost forgot to worry about the dentist on my left. I mean, worrying as to how he'd get through his speech about me. He knew, I was certain, more about tooth decay than anyone else in the United States but, after all, it was only *one* of the professions. I had finally—after trying to explain that I was a writer (w-r-i-t-e-r) and that, no, I'd never appeared in *Dental Hygiene*—taken the pencil away from him. "Maybe I better write it down for you," I'd said, kindly. "It'll go faster that way."

But I needn't have worried. My dentist friend from Cleveland did beautifully. "On my right," he announced, "is

Lucile Hardman—or I mean she used to be—and she used to be pretty sharp on the ukelele. Now she's a—ah—writer." He peered down at the card uncertainly and then added: "At least, that's what it says here."

Who, pray, could have summed it up better?

Dibs and Dabs

Happy Birthday to You!

AUGUST THE sixth, as everyone knows, is the date when the first atomic bomb exploded over Hiroshima. August the sixth, as everyone knows, is also the Feast of the Transfiguration and the Introit for the day reads: "Thy lightnings lit up the world; the earth shook and trembled."

Now, there is obviously a lot of symbolism involved here, although it escapes me for the moment, and a certain Father M. of Notre Dame has even written a scholarly dissertation on the subject. I would like to point out, however, that Father M.'s thesis is incomplete. In fact, he overlooked what you might call his ace card in working out all that symbolism. August the sixth, along with the Transfiguration and the atomic bomb explosion, is also MY BIRTHDAY!

All that business about the earth trembling and the heavens lighting up takes on immediately a new and powerful significance, especially when you consider—and now get this!—that even the name Lucile means "light." ("Light-headed," says my husband, but he's prejudiced. Officially, Lucile means "light." Period.)

But isn't all this terribly interesting? I would, matter of fact, take over Father M.'s material—which was certainly mighty slipshod, leaving out my birthday—and do it up brown, but you know how it is. He might be sensitive. So, I think I'll just content myself with a few of my *personal* reactions to August the sixth. No symbolism will be used. Just stark facts.

I have, over the years, greeted August the sixth with various mixed feelings but when I hit the fortieth milestone—why, my feelings weren't mixed a bit. I just wanted to lie down and die, that was all. *I* knew what was ahead of me, all right, and so why didn't someone just shoot me, right on the spot, and spare me all the middle age misery awaiting me? And don't think I hadn't been boning up on all the symptoms: fatigue, flushes, pains in joints, headaches, digestive disturbances, moodiness, bawling over nothing, fears, insomnia, dropping dishes, loss of memory. (Even though, as someone has said: "One good thing about my type of mind—loss of memory will scarcely be noticeable.")

August the sixth might be the Feast of the Transfiguration, I brooded, but the only transfiguration in store for me was— well, *why* wouldn't someone just shoot me and get it over with? But since none of my fair-weather friends stepped forward and volunteered to do the dirty work, I was thrown back on my own resources. Since I apparently had to go on living, I decided to give myself a birthday party to cheer myself up, and invite my guests to bring me presents. Gag presents, I qualified. Funny stuff, to tide me somehow through the zero hour.

However, the only present that lingers in my memory,

which is already going to pot, was on the stark side. Handing me a dainty flask of *Old Grand-Dad*, the gentleman said soberly: "This is not a gag. It's the only sensible thing I can think of for a woman turning forty." (And he might well have added, like Captain Queeg in *The Caine Mutiny*: "I kid you not.")

The fortieth birthday is the worst, though. After that, I find that a certain numbness sets in: like having a tooth frozen so that you don't *too* much mind the dentist's jabbings. Occasionally there are even pleasant little happenings: like the campus professor who always greets me with a "Well, hullo there! How are you, lassie?" to warm my heart. It always makes me feel like such a wee slip of a lass that I *do* hope he doesn't have Lassie, canine daughter of Rin-Tin-Tin, in mind.

Anyhow, this past August the sixth—when the earth again trembled and I turned forty-three—I scarcely even noticed it. I was too busy watching the earth tremble and the heavens light up as Miss Victory, of Tampa, Florida, was shot out of a cannon at the annual Police Show. All of which should make it very clear, by now, that August the sixth is a great day for explosions.

Come, Come to the Refrigerator

The power of the printed word—for better, for worse—is practically unlimited, but have you ever noticed how, in particular, it affects your taste buds? Actually, it's quite a moral problem.

For some women, it's the richly illustrated recipes in the slick women's magazines—the glazed strawberry tarts, the delicate lemon chiffon pies, the shining chocolate éclairs—

that excite their little taste buds and send them, willy-nilly, out to the kitchen. For others, it's the snob appeal to their taste buds that is their undoing. Such as those ads in *The New Yorker* that start out: "For that charmed circle who count not the cost, this superlative beer was brewed without thought of expense," et cetera.

Now, this sort of temptation leaves me unshaken. It's too crude an appeal to my lower appetites. I remain above it— cool, austere, and with my soul in my hands—like St. Thomas Aquinas when confronted with the courtesan. What play havoc with *my* taste buds, and reduce me to a state of drooling non-control are the fictional accounts of dire privation and hunger. Completely unstrung by my sympathy for the book characters, and vicariously sharing in their hunger pangs, I immediately start craving whatever food item is under discussion.

It doesn't have to be a *tasty* food item, you understand, but just the one that the author has happened to land on. Such as the radishes in *Gone With The Wind*. How well do I remember the starving Scarlett O'Hara when she discovered some radishes growing on the war-ravished plantation of Tara. They were "old, coarse, and peppery" but I could fairly feel my eyes watering with enjoyment as I, along with Scarlett, wolfed down those radishes, the earth of Tara still clinging to them. I didn't even find myself wishing for a dash of salt.

Then, in *Giants In The Earth*, Per Hansa and his wife Beret and children—while crossing the plains in ox-pulled covered wagons—had only a bowl of porridge at the end of a hard day's travelling. One evening, as a rare delicacy, Beret had added a spoonful of molasses to the porridge and Per Hansa's eyes had lit up with dull pleasure, while the children had clapped their tiny hands with joy. So, I found myself wonder-

ing how *my* family would like some delicious bowls of porridge and molasses, instead of the pork roast I'd planned on
having, for their evening meal. Certainly, *my* mouth was
watering for porridge. (By the by, just what *is* porridge? The
same as Cream of Wheat?)

Then, just the other evening, I was reading about Edith
Stein—the philosopher, Jewess, Catholic, and Carmelite nun
who was murdered in a concentration camp—and, once again,
a chance paragraph upset my taste buds. Miss Stein was describing, harmlessly enough, a walking trip she had once
taken as a student through the forests around Göttingen,
Germany. How utterly delicious, she had written, were the
provisions in her *rucksack*: a loaf of black bread, a packet of
butter, a bit of sausage, and a bar of chocolate. For no earthly
good reason, I suddenly found myself craving a slice of black
bread. Of course, we never keep the stuff in the house, but,
fortunately, there *was* a slice of light rye, somewhat darkened
by age, in the breadbox. I carried it out on the steps of the
back porch and sat there gnawing it, meanwhile imagining
myself overlooking a valley in Göttingen. It tasted delicious.

It was Dorothy Day's *The Long Loneliness*, though, that almost led me into mortal sin. I made the mistake of reading
it during Lent, with its no-eating-betwixt-meals restriction,
and I don't know when I've been so sorely tempted. Miss Day
was so very graphic in her descriptions, and so terribly hun-
gry herself at the time, that I could literally feel my stomach
caving in on me. Could I, I wondered, get a special dispensation from Father Higgins until I'd finished the book? Knowing my pastor as I do, though, I decided to spare my breath
and just write in and complain to Dorothy herself. She might
be leading *others* to high sanctity, I wrote her, but she had me

wrestling with all sorts of evil spirits: spirits who kept whispering, "Come, come to the refrigerator."

Miss Day wrote back, sympathetically: "If you really want
to suffer excruciatingly, read the book *Hunger* by Knut Ham-
sun." This promised treat I am saving for the future. . . .
say, a raw winter day when I'm in bed with a sore throat and
can't possibly swallow a thing. I expect to suffer quite
horribly.

Meet More Interesting People

I recently perused, with considerable relish, an article in
the *Cosmopolitan* that was called "So You Want To Be An
Author!" and that carried the fascinating sub-title: "Like
to get in on the thirty million dollars a year paid to writers?"
But what fascinated me even more than that sub-title was
the news that an estimated five million people yearn to be
authors and that there are perhaps five million more who
haven't admitted it. (How these statistics were arrived at,
I wouldn't know. Anyone come to the door and ask *you*?)

Anyhow, I find there is something alarming in the thought
of all this seething frustration right in our midst. It just isn't
healthy, especially when you consider the *Cosmopolitan*
article's definition of writing: "a soul-satisfying expression
of human vanity." Ten million people walking the streets,
with all this bottled-up human vanity, are a veritable powder
keg. The day may come when they will seize the presses and
force editors, at the point of a bayonet, to print their stuff or
else. (I, myself, have often toyed with the idea of using a
bayonet on an editor but have always, at the last minute,
settled for a stinging letter—following, I guess, the principle
that the ball-point is mightier than the bayonet.)

But come the revolution or not, I am frankly more worried about the five million people who *won't* admit they want to be authors than I am about the others. They, the secretive and furtive ones, are going to find themselves stretching out on psychiatrists' couches and paying a nice fat fee to become integrated. And while the psychiatrist may *think* he's helping them by untwisting their childhood traumas this won't be the case at all. Any help or relief that the patient experiences will be based solely on the fact that he, at long last, is feeling like an author as he dictates his memoirs. Actually, all that would be needed to adjust the poor wretch at one fell stroke would be for the psychiatrist to present the patient with a printed and leather-bound edition of his subconscious ramblings. This tangible proof of his authorship—carelessly displayed, say, in the center of the coffee table—would do as much for a man's morale as a mounted moosehead over the fireplace.

Technically, a book of this sort would be referred to, in the publishing business, as a "vanity publishing" but so what? Vanity is what we're dealing with, isn't it? Besides, it wouldn't be much more expensive than pouring money down the drain by taking endless correspondence lessons. Now it's true that most writing courses are a racket, or at best pretty futile, but I felt that the *Cosmopolitan* author chose a very poor illustration to prove his point. He gave, as an example of the advertising bait used, the following ad:

"Does the outdoors call to you today? Then take your work to the beach or the mountains for as a writer you can work anywhere, anytime. You are your own boss! No working when you are not in the mood! Meet more interesting people!"

Technically speaking, truer words were never spoken. For instance, if the outdoors calls to me and I whimsically decide to take my typewriter to the beach, what's to stop me? Nothing, except mosquitoes and my three children pouring sand down my back and about three hundred bathers gawking at me and my Corona. Or do I prefer to take my work to the mountains? Here again there is nothing to stop me except that I happen to live smack in the middle of the United States and the nearest mountain range is about as handy, as far as I'm concerned, as the Pyrenees.

But, and this is the important point, am I my own boss? The captain of my ship, the master of my soul? Certainly. There's no time-clock to punch around *our* house, let me tell you. There's no peace or quiet, either, but that *Cosmopolitan* man was just talking about time-clocks.

And as to the last bit of allurement: "Meet more interesting people!" Let no one, I beg of you, try to tell you that *this* isn't true. The mailman comes by every day, approximately at one o'clock, and he is easily one of the most interesting people in my life: a perpetual Man of Mystery; a dispassionate dispenser of Good and Evil tidings from editors; a sphinx-like bearer of either fan mail or poison pen letters from readers.

That's Simple Enough

I find that there is something very fascinating, in a horrid sort of way, in those little boxed-in newspaper ads—generally advertising patent medicines and pills—that leap out, as if from ambush, at the reader. You come to the end of a column on, say, the Taft-Hartley bill or an editorial plea to put Christ back into Christmas and, suddenly, *this* leaps out at you in black bold type: "You May Have Pinworms And

Not Know It!" Or, "Distressed By Belching, Heartburn, Gas Pains?" Or, "Is Fiery Itch Driving You Nuts?" Or, "False Teeth Slip And Chafe?" Or, "Intestines All Plugged Up?"

The sheer poetry of these little ads, not to mention the attractive images they conjure up, is enough to *give* a person gas pains right on the spot. Even the prettier little jingles, such as "When sour stomach makes you queasy, *Tums* correct it mighty easy," have a way of stripping the last shred of dignity from a man. (Man, created in the image of God, destined to live forever.) None of us mind receiving the Ash Wednesday smudge on our foreheads, with its "dust to dust" reminder, but it is far more sobering to think of ourselves as a race of belching and plugged-up creatures, suffering from sour stomach and slipping dental plates. It rather makes me wonder if perhaps these ad writers aren't a subversive Moscow element: undermining our morale, having so little regard for the dignity of man. . . . !

Yet, even though I cringe from those jarring little ads, I still find myself composing a similar ad—mentally, that is—whenever I read the poetry of Charles Péguy. I hope Péguy (now dead) will forgive me, for I love him dearly, but I invariably think of him in terms of: "Feeling nervous, scrupulous, and spiritually upset? Can't sleep nights, worrying about the state of the union? Read Péguy's *God Speaks!* Money back guarantee if not delighted!"

Now, Péguy would perhaps be dangerous reading for a calloused and rip-roaring fugitive from Alcatraz—who needed a good stiff shot of the fear of the Lord rather than a spiritual sedative—but I am assuming, perhaps rashly, that my readers are *not* fugitives from Alcatraz. And I say that Péguy is both a treat and a treatment for those good but harassed souls who, as Péguy puts it, "work well but sleep

badly, who are all aglow in their beds with unrest and fever."
That is, those good people who have the best motives in the
world—and perhaps work their apostolic fingers to the bone
laboring in the vineyard—but who can't relax, at the end of
the day, and let Divine Providence take over. Writes Péguy:

> The man who concocts plans, the one who inside himself,
>   in his own head,
> Works for tomorrow like a hired laborer,
> Works dreadfully like a slave making an everlasting wheel
>   go round
> (And between you and me like a fool),
> Well, that man is in no way agreeable to me, says God.
> He who abandons himself, I love. He who does not abandon
>   himself, I don't love.
> That's simple enough.

And it is simple, once you see the paradox. That is, the
need to be both zealous and relaxed, earnest but not grim.
It's certainly nothing new by way of spiritual guidance, for
we know all this in the back of our minds, but our "feelings"
and our "nerves" are forever tripping us up. And Péguy's
way of putting this across is particularly effective because
of the device he uses of having God the Father express, in
simple and colloquial language, what he thinks of us and
our antics. "I know man well. It is I who made him. A funny
creature," God starts out, but in no place does Péguy have
God sink to the level of those ad writers I was talking about.
God may refer to us occasionally as "funny creatures" or
"poor creatures" but he leaves us with our dignity intact; he
doesn't once mention our sour stomachs and bad breath; he
is kind enough to notice only our souls. Indeed, in one lovely
passage, God observes:

All the prostrations in the world
Are not worth the beautiful upright attitude of a free man
    as he kneels. All the submission, all the dejection in the
    world
Are not equal in value to the soaring up point,
The beautiful straight soaring up of one single invocation
From a love that is free.

Doesn't *that* rather give you a more pleasant picture of
    Man?

Doing It the Hard Way

It always annoys me when I read gloomy treatises that
imply that Catholicism, as a way of life, is synonymous with
suffering; that to join the Church is just *asking* for trouble;
that suffering is, so to speak, the Catholic's passport to
heaven. Certainly, it may well *prove* his passport, in a given
case, but that's beside the point. I'm talking about suffering
as suffering, not how one faces up to it. Anyhow, this
Johnny-One-Note stress on all the misery and tribulation that
automatically await the baptized Catholic, much as if it were
part of canon law, is annoying on several scores.

For one thing, it gives outsiders the wrong impression of
a religion that is fundamentally joyous; where all of the
seven sacraments are designed to make and keep us happy,
not miserable. (Unless, of course, you want to be a funny-
guy and except the Sacrament of Matrimony.) But my main
point is that this idea that Catholics have a corner on suffering
just isn't the truth; just doesn't hold water.

Everyone faces suffering. Everyone in the world is wide-
open to all sorts of suffering—no matter what his creed or

lack of creed—and it's the Catholic religion that makes suffering *easier,* not harder. How? By looking it smack in the face
and seeing suffering for what it is in the light of reality;
not a "good" or a "blessing" in itself but capable of being
turned into a tremendous good; not a senseless affliction—
with no possible rhyme or reason behind it—but a definite
part of the over-all plan, as seen from all eternity.

Nor is this just a bit of wishful thinking to make us "feel"
better; feel less like trapped rats. To *deny* this doctrine of
Divine Providence, this doctrine that nothing happens by
chance, is to say that God has lost control of His universe.
That He, God, started something He couldn't handle; that
He, God, no longer has the foggiest idea as to what all is
going on. It's perfectly okay to criticize Eisenhower or Senator McCarthy if you want, but to criticize God is to deny
his very existence. So let's go on from there, with God
definitely established as God, his attributes intact.

Now I am no theologian, as all my friends will eagerly
testify, but it strikes me that the Catholic Church—when it
comes to this business of suffering—walks off with all the
honors. It so *thoroughly* covers the waterfront; so thor-
oughly understands man's nature and needs. It prepares you
for suffering by giving you tiny little doses of disciplined
mortification: the Lenten regulations, the no-hamburger on
Friday, the piling out of a warm bed on a rainy morning to
attend Mass, the going without your precious cup of coffee
in order to receive Communion. All this is what outsiders
sometimes think of as a senseless hardship—these little dis-
ciplines and regulations—although they, themselves, would
gladly suffer the tortures of the damned for a worldly motive.
Consider, for example, the years of rigorous training a person will undergo in order to swim the English Channel.

But my main point is that the Church, when it comes to *real* suffering, offers such tremendously solid comfort in so many different ways. Even a helter-skelter and hasty listing is quite impressive: the Catholic habit of "offering it up" (for nothing is more painful than *wasted* suffering); the weight-lifting comfort of the sacraments, especially confession and communion; the power of the Mass for special intentions; the dazzling variety of saints to appeal to for help; the unlimited spiritual reading that's there for the reading; the almost blind comfort (for a mind too dazed by grief or weakened from illness to function properly) in just *holding* a rosary or a crucifix; the miraculous shrines, like Lourdes, for the lame and the blind and the halt; the spiritual joining of hands, by way of letters and their own magazines, for chronic invalids belonging to the Shut-In League; the incalculable peace and comfort of a bedside priest to administer Extreme Unction. . . .

Yet perhaps as much as anything, I like the way Catholics will—without the diffidence and embarrassment that a Protestant would feel—ask their friends to storm heaven on their behalf.

So, all things considered, I definitely prefer (if I must suffer and I guess I must) to do it the "hard" Catholic way.

A Man's World

All wives, if the dreadful truth were known, have had their moments—or at least *a* moment in their married lives—when they could gladly and cheerfully strangle their husbands with their bare hands. I strongly suspect this can also work vice versa, for I've noticed a peculiar gleam in my husband's eye whenever I suggest rearranging the living room furniture, but I can only report my own criminal tendencies. *My* moment came shortly before the birth of my third child, and I'm sure that any all-woman jury—if I *had* come up for trial—would have understood perfectly. Even nodded sympathetically as they piped up with nostalgic and similar experiences of their own.

A pregnant woman, especially during the last long month of waiting, is a touchy and irrational creature; a creature to be handled with kid gloves. And I was particularly in need of kid gloves, as the zero hour approached, because it meant facing my third Caesarian operation. I had the general feeling —shared, incidentally, by a goodly number of medicos— that Caesarians were a necessary evil and that, whereas two of them were okay, you were skating on thin ice thereafter. Also the fact that I was slated to enter the hospital on the day after Christmas only added to the pathos of it all. Heaven knows I *tried* to feel Madonna-ish and in full accord with the liturgical cycle, as I awaited my Christmas babe, but I honestly felt more like a man on Death Row. So they were going to let me have a last Merry Christmas, eh? Order a last hearty meal before walking the last mile?

It was in this jolly frame of mind that I awoke one morning, around four A.M., shortly before Christmas. It was an old story, this not being able to sleep, and I heaved a weary sigh as I slipped my swollen feet into a pair of my husband's old bedroom slippers. What, I wondered, should I do for my nightly entertainment? Play solitaire? Raid the refrigerator? Work jig-saw puzzles? Clean out the kitchen cupboards?

It was certainly a man's world, I thought glumly, as I shuffled downstairs in the outsize slippers and left my husband peacefully sleeping. Was there, in all creation, a more infuriating sight than an expectant father—sleeping like a log—while the expectant mother padded around the house like a lost banshee?

I padded over to the desk, switched on the desk lamp, and discovered a note from my husband staring up at me. "Darling," it read, "if you can't sleep and come downstairs, would you care to look over this poem I've written? I thought of sending it to *Sign* magazine."

Now, I am not at my critical best at four A.M. and all I needed, to blow my top, was one look at the title: *The Expectant Father Prays For A Boy*. It was at this precise moment that the blood rushed to my head; that I longed to rush upstairs and throttle the expectant father. I secretly wanted a boy, too, but did my husband have to put it in *writing*? And who did he think I was, anyway? A magician who could pull rabbits out of a hat? And who did he think *he* was—he, who was sleeping so peacefully upstairs—that he could put in this royal and Sultan-like order for a male child?

With blurred vision, I picked up the Sultan's lyrical request:

> Lord, I can do without a boy.
> The girls you sent us have been apple sweet,
> Voices ever in song or cry or laughter,
> And they have bells upon their glancing feet.
> Lord, I can do without a boy.
>
> Lord, girls are just as good as boys.
> True, they can't run so fast or hike so far;
> They'll bait their hook until they enter high
>   school
> And they have little sense to drive a car.
> Yet girls are good as boys.

> Lord, girls are good as gold.
> But I can do without too large a hoard.
> Two menfolk in a house could get a hearing
> Where one is all too easily ignored—
> Though girls are good as gold.
>
> Lord, I can do without a boy.
> Surely, a boy might grieve me night and day.
> There's plenty of room to think about Saint
>   Joseph
> And how his lad was needed for the Way.
> Lord, it is yours to say.

"Lord, it is yours to say." Even though my husband had the decency to admit this little factor, he wasn't fooling me for one little minute. I *still* felt this intolerable responsibility to come through with flying colors.

With tears streaming down my face, murder in my heart, and the weight of the world on my shoulders, I shuffled out to the kitchen. How was I to know in that dark hour, as I mournfully munched a bologna sandwich, that young Danny was on the way; that my incredulous ears were to hear those blessed words: "IT'S A BOY!" Or that I would one day think my husband's poem was really rather sweet, after all.

Hoo-Ray for Eddie!

Frank Leahy, at the end of the Notre Dame football season, is always a nervously exhausted man but not until this past fall, when *I* become involved with a football team, could I properly sympathize with him. I don't mean to say, of course,

that I actually had to coach the eighth grade football squad
at Holy Cross parochial school—or even serve as water boy
—but I feel, modestly, that my role was not to be lightly dis-
missed. They also serve who only stand and suffer, and my
contribution to the 1952 football season was a thirteen year
old cheerleader daughter.

This meant that our home came to serve as the base of
operation for the cheerleading squad and, in due time, our
living room developed all the privacy of Grand Central
Station. ("Ideal location," the real estate man had said, as
we signed the papers. "Only a few blocks from Holy Cross!")
Our regular family life, and meals, came to be sandwiched
in between the really important things in life, such as prac-
ticing bigger and better yells to keep up the team's morale.
No one, I might add, seemed too concerned about the morale
of Mr. and Mrs. Hasley.

Now I am perfectly willing to admit that the Holy Cross
cheerleaders, in their white corduroy skirts and blue sweaters,
with bells on their shoestrings, were as cute as buttons as
they went through their paces. All I'm saying is that I still
wake up at night and think I hear voices chanting: "Hoo-ray
for Eddie! Hoo-ray for Eddie! Someone in the crowd is
yelling hoo-ray for Eddie! One, two, three, four, who you
gonna yell for? Eddie, that's who!" The special charm about
this particular chant is that it is then followed by a rhythmic
"da-da-da-da"—before repeating the same thing for all the
rest of the eighth grade squad. All told, it only takes about
a half hour to run through.

Anyhow, when I was asked to be a chaperone this fall for
their first Victory Dance over at Holy Cross, I could scarcely
—what with my own flesh and blood being such an integral
part of the victory—refuse my services. Besides which, I

reasoned that my ear drums were by then sufficiently condi-
tioned to stand the gaff. This, as it turned out, was merely
wishful thinking. I had forgotten to count on the tile walls
of the room making the dance records, not to mention the
inevitable "Hoo-ray for Eddie" cheer performed during inter-
mission, sound like a scene from *Hellzapoppin'*. This impression was heightened when one of the boys, in horsing
around, accidentally sent the pay telephone, installed by
the P.T.A., crashing to the floor. (Mine was the enviable job
of reporting to the pastor: "Sorry, Father, but the wall telephone is now on the floor in the kitchen.")

Moreover, any illusions I may have had that the boys, like
little gentlemen, would be *dying* to dance with the girls,
were rudely shattered. The gentlemen, lined up against the
tile wall, couldn't be pried loose for love or money and, this
I learned the hard way, is the chief function of a chaperone:
to wheedle, taunt, threaten, or even *push* the boys onto the
dance floor. Quoting the slogan of a well-known dancing
school, I kept muttering, "If You Can Walk, You Can Dance"
but they didn't seem too sure they could even walk. As Marce-
line Cox has said: Little ladies may be born, but little gentlemen are hewn, like monuments, out of solid resistance.

Once they finally got into the spirit of the dance, though,
all their latent chivalry rose to the surface. One young gentleman from the seventh grade, who came up to about my
waist, even politely offered to push *me* around to the strains
of *Slaughter On Tenth Avenue*. Another young gentleman,
standing as stiff as a poker before me, hurriedly recited:
"My name is Harold Schmidt. My mother said I should
always introduce myself to the chaperone. So if you ever
meet my mother, will you tell her I done it?" It was a manly

little speech, only slightly spoiled by my having to yell over the din: "Eh? What's that?"

The strange roaring persisted in my ears for several hours after the dance but there was, naturally, nothing in medical science to help me. You can soak your aching feet in mustard water; apply a hot pad to a wrenched back; but what in the world can you do about beaten-up eardrums? Imagine my emotions, therefore, when I was again asked to be a chaperone the following week.

"But you didn't win the game," I protested faintly. "St. Adalbert's beat you by twenty-two points. Why a Victory Dance?"

"But this is to be a Cheer-up Dance," explained my cheer-leader daughter.

You Aren't Alone

A parish priest, at the end of a hard day, is inclined to take a rather dim view of humanity. This certainly was the case, anyhow, when I recently dropped in at the rectory to check up on a few theological angles for a talk I was preparing.

"Don't you think," I started off brightly, "that women, on the whole, tend to be scrupulous and nervous and to let this take the joy out of their religion? Don't you think they could well afford a little more—uh—spiritual gaiety?"

My pastor regarded me with a jaundiced eye. "Frankly," he said, in a gloomy voice, "I could use a little more scrupulosity around this parish. In fact, I'd *like* it—I'd *welcome* it." (He didn't exactly add, "Spiritual gaiety, pah!" but I got the general idea all right.)

I had, indeed, hit him at the wrong moment. It seems

that, just as I'd walked in the front door, he had hung up
the telephone receiver on a conversation that had left him
rather dazed. "Is it true what I've heard about your daughter?" he had asked this particular parishioner. "Has she
really married outside the Church?"

"Gee, I don't know," the mother had said placidly. "But
I'll ask her, Father."

And right on the heels of *this*, I had waltzed merrily in and
asked if he didn't think women were too scrupulous! (Nice
timing, Hasley, old girl.) Just the same, I still stick to my
story that scruples are a common affliction and I base this
theory on the many letters I've received from women. In particular, I remember receiving a tortured letter from North
Dakota that would have made your heart bleed. "In the
name of charity," she had wound up, "*please* tell me where
I can get this book you recommended called *Pardon And
Peace*." And then there was a postscript, apparently tacked
on as an afterthought: "I have nine children."

Personally, I didn't see how she possibly had *time* to be
scrupulous, what with nine kids milling around, but apparently scruples, like virus X, can hit anyone. And while
in some cases I would say that a bottle of Lydia Pinkham
or several stiff hormone injections were indicated to handle
the female nervous system, I think an excellent all-around
remedy is plain theology. Namely, the theological principle
that feelings and emotions are relatively unimportant and
that what counts, in the eyes of the Lord, is the purity of
your intentions. It is also comforting to remember that perfection, per se, isn't so important as the just plugging *after*
perfection.

This is the thing to hang onto when you find yourself
screaming like a fishwife at the children, five minutes after

having made your morning offering. Or when you get that sinking feeling that your confessions are so hopelessly inadequate, and even downright dopey, that they couldn't possibly be any good. Or when you find yourself, right at the communion rail, worrying about the Sunday pot roast. Or when you one day have all the fervor of a St. Joan of Arc and the next day are so spiritually blank that you can scarcely recognize yourself.

It is a tremendous comfort, I think, to realize that *everyone* has moments like this and that you are not alone. Even the great St. Teresa of Avila, you know, said that at one time God meant no more to her than a three-letter word. But it was also Teresa who said: "Patient endurance attaineth to all things."

This might well apply, it seems to me, to those horrid stretches of aridity, the wrestling with distractions, the torment of scruples, the utter lack of any sensible consolations when it comes to "feeling" nice and holy. After all, if the spiritual life were a perpetual honeymoon—full of thrills and emotional jags and walking on air—there would be scant opportunity *really* to show your love for God. Or, for that matter, ever to become a mature Catholic.

What Flavor?

This is to be a gripe, pure and simple, and with no spiritual overtones whatsoever. I would like to say that (with the exception of my husband, who will eat anything that's stuck in front of his face) I have the most utterly disgusting family in the United States to cook for and, one of these days, I may just resign. A person can bear only so much and I feel a certain rapport with people who have, with a fine abandon, tossed their thankless jobs overboard: such as that bus driver in Chicago who, during the Christmas rush, reached the end of his tether. Over the protests of his alarmed passengers, he drove the bus across town to the car barn, stepped out, and announced simply: "I quit." And then there was the mail carrier whose shining moment came when he tossed his bag of mail into a snowdrift and just walked off. "I got tired," he explained to the U.S. postal authorities when they finally caught up with him.

All this I can understand perfectly. Of course, I can't openly *advocate* such actions but I would like to go on record as being sympathetic. Trying to find a vegetable or salad or even dessert that everyone in the family will eat without moaning, has left me feeling very mellow toward all others who lead lives of quiet desperation. I find that there is something very discouraging, to put it mildly, in having a child announce calmly "I hate that!" before you even get the dish set down on the table. Or in asking "What's dessert?" before they even get the napkin unfolded and then, upon being told "Ice cream," suspiciously demanding "What flavor?" (Once upon a time ice cream, in *any* flavor, was considered a treat.) Equally discouraging, when it comes to trying out new recipes, is to have a child poke at the food and say, "Creepers, what's this?"—much as if he expected a garter snake to crawl out.

Please understand that I am not one of those cooks who insist on, or even expect, any glowing comments on my culinary efforts. All I'm saying is that, after preparing a decent meal, I expect a little cooperation: a lifting of the fork to the mouth *without* acting as if they were signing their own death warrant.

Hence, I would like to take issue with Mr. Joseph Breig who, in a recent column, wrote that one should *never* make a child eat anything he doesn't feel like eating. I have just one question to ask Mr. Breig: "Does *Mrs.* Breig, after slaving over a hot stove, see eye to eye with you on this? Is *she* perfectly willing to throw a hot meal out the back door and hand the children a jar of peanut butter?"

At any rate, my own reaction to Mr. Breig's column was to tear it up immediately. Things are bad enough around our house without letting my family read a dangerous thing like *that*. Life would become unbearable with my children throwing Breig in my face: "Yah, yah. Mr. Breig says we don't hafta eat anything we don't want. So there!"

But before I give up the ship (that is, plunk a jar of peanut butter in the middle of the table and walk out the front door), I have one more trick up my sleeve. An article in the newspaper the other evening gave me new inspiration, new hope. It occurred to me, after I got through gagging, that if I were to read this article aloud at the dinner table, it just *might* make them appreciate the kind of food I'm serving up. You see, this article was describing some choice recipes that the housewives in Bangkok, Siam, delight in and I would like, if your stomachs are strong enough, to quote a few passages:

"Ant eggs rank high in Siamese gourmet preferences, according to Mom Raja Krukrit Pramong, grandson of the IV King of Siam. The best variety of ant egg is always sold pickled and then mixed with spices and sugar, chopped green onions, and Chinese parsley. Another great favorite is the giant waterbug, with the male of the species being the more flavorsome. After heads and wings are removed, the bugs are pounded with cloves of garlic and, if desired, lime juice can be added. Another favorite delicacy is caterpillars, usually pickled in brine, but considered more desirable when fresh. If you are fortunate enough to get them alive, then drop them into a large bowl of thick, creamy, coconut milk and let them drink it all up. Next, sauté a few cloves of crushed garlic over a low fire and add two cups of the caterpillars. Serve with fish sauce and pepper."

Maybe after getting a load of *that*, my family will settle down happily to some plain old-fashioned American victuals and consider themselves lucky. Yet I can't help wondering, at the same time, how those Siamese housewives make out. Do they ever have a scene like the following?

Child: "What's for supper, Mama?"

Mama: "Some lovely fresh caterpillars, dear."

Child: "What flavor? Are they brown caterpillars or the yellow ones?"

Mama: "Brown ones, dear."

Child: "I HATE brown caterpillars. Just make me an ant egg sandwich."

There's Always a Catch

My daughter Susan recently reported to me, in high disgust, that she had just finished reading a story about a saint who had, at the tender age of five, taken the vow of chastity and who, on another occasion, had driven a nail in her head by way of mortification. "And then they tell us we're supposed to imitate the saints!" she concluded scornfully.

Well, if you ask me, it's little isolated tidbits like this—be they true or false—that give sanctity a black eye and put the poor saints in the same category as side-show freaks: Freddie the Fire Eater or Rudolph the Rubber Man. Certainly, driving nails in one's head (a dubious procedure at best) does not represent the Alpha and Omega of sanctity. Yet these spectacular little items, be they true or false, have a way of sidetracking the reader so that the main thing—the *essence* of sanctity—is lost by the wayside. And that essence, of course, is simply this: abandonment to God's holy will.

So, seeing as how sanctity is so simple, what are we waiting for? What's holding us up? Didn't St. Augustine himself make it *extremely* simple with his carefree little dictum: "Love God, and do as you please"?

Well, the catch (and there's always a catch) is that we all have our *own* versions as to how to love God. Moreover, we all have an odd tendency, be it conscious or unconscious, to interpret God's will in the light of our *own* will. Of course, we can always come up with a "Well, it must be God's will," as we gaze down at the corpse in the funeral home or read about a volcano erupting in Japan, but that's a relatively easy response. It's not nearly so easy to figure out God's will in our day to day living for there is, unfortunately, no blanket rule that covers everyone. Each individual on God's green earth has to figure out, through trial and error, what God expects from *him*. And it is through trial and error (and frequently falling flat on your face) that one gradually develops a certain sensitivity as regards his own particular wave length. (E.g., you may secretly feel you were cut out to be a contemplative, destined to hit the peaks in prayer, and then God so fills your life with noise and work that it practically makes your back teeth rattle. Contemplation, per se, becomes an obvious luxury and, equally obvious, the noise and the work are supposed to become *your* "sacrament of the Present Moment.")

Anyhow, it is through prayer, spiritual direction, common

horse sense, Catholic reading, and sharing experiences with others in your particular state of life, that you gradually begin to see a pattern for yourself. This is a tremendous subject—so tremendous that I feel like a mouse nibbling at a mountain of cheese—but I would at least like to emphasize one big point. Personal sanctity is a *personal* business and only God can peer behind the scenes and safely pass judgment. And, to pass from individuals to families, what is right for one Christian family is not necessarily right for another. We are not all called upon to embrace Holy Poverty, à la Leon Bloy, or to have a dozen children or to go in for the rural life or to live (by way of "protest") in a Negro slum district. The right pattern, or vocation, for one family would be suicide for another. Moreover, our children are *individuals*—not just lumps of clay for us to hammer into set molds—and, aside from trying to instill general Christian principles into the little dears, we have no right to demand more of them than even the Church would demand. Just because *you* choose to live as St. John the Baptist is no guarantee that your children, as they sprout into individuals, are going to thrive on honey and locusts.

Yet there is a tendency among certain Catholics to point the finger of scorn at other Catholics who appear (I say *appear*) to be wallowing in a bourgeois mediocrity and not accepting the challenge to live as the unsolicitous lilies of the field. Yet do you, or I, actually know what goes on behind the scenes? The hidden crosses? The perhaps even stark heroism? Can you, for instance, say that a necessary continence in marriage—for valid and even heart-breaking reasons—is less heroic than the "abandonment" of those who obviously have a vocation to raise a large family? Does a hanging slip or a bedraggled head scarf, on a female Catholic apostle, necessarily indicate a holy detachment? Is a Bendix washer in the home a clear-cut indication that a gross materialism rules the day?

In brief, judge not. It's a risky business that involves more balance and more compassion (not to mention an All-Seeing Eye) than most of us can claim. I also suspect that charity towards one's neighbor and the avoidance of rash judgment will rate higher—in the eyes of the Lord—than any austere heroism of our own. Maybe even higher than driving nails in one's head.

Short Stories

"*I Remember Mama*"

IT'S FUNNY, sometimes, the way you can go along knowing a person—and thinking you've got all the depths and angles figured out—and then suddenly discovering you haven't even pricked the surface.

Take Mildred. She's been my hairdresser for the past three years, ever since I moved into this neighborhood. I don't know whether you know her place over on Belmont Avenue or not—the "Elite Beauty Shoppe" it's called—although there's nothing very elite about it. It's just the usual sort of neighborhood beauty shop: a bowl of dusty paper roses at the front window, tan plaster walls covered with ads for tonics and permanents, the usual chromium chairs, and the usual stacks of true confession and movie magazines. Even Mildred seems to be part of the regular equipment, to blend right in with those paper roses and tan walls and chromium chairs.

Dish-water blonde, I guess you'd call Mildred, although I can't actually describe her very well. She's just one of those persons who don't impress you much one way or another.

No, the only thing that isn't strictly regulation about the

Elite Beauty Shoppe is Bitzi, and Bitzi is a character I could get along without very nicely. Bitzi is an ancient, cross, fat poodle dog: the apple of Mildred's eye and the thorn in my flesh. I've got nothing against dogs as dogs, understand, but this Bitzi is like a punch-drunk ex-pugilist.

I sometimes suspect that Bitzi rests up and gets in condition during the rest of the week and then, as soon as I appear, goes into her act to test my spirit. Around and around the room she'll trot, in maddening circles, wheezing like a suction pump, with her sharp toenails going click, click, click on the linoleum floor. I have even, on particularly trying days, offered up the irritation of Bitzi's clicking toenails and loud wheezing like St. Thérèse used to offer up the old nun who sat in front of her in chapel, rattling her beads and praying in loud asthmatic gusts.

Only don't get the idea that I spend my time in prayer at the Elite Beauty Shoppe. No, indeed. I catch up on Hollywood. Mildred is as absorbed in the latest loves and hair-dos of Lana Turner and Rita Hayworth as a Brooklyn kid is with the batting averages of the Dodgers. So I generally flip through a movie magazine (one literary notch higher, I figure, than a confession magazine) while Mildred simultaneously sets my pin curls, peers over my shoulder, and conducts a running commentary on the lives and loves of Beverly Hills. Every so often she'll reach over and point, with the wet comb, to a coming attraction (always dynamic! always colossal! always epic!) and heave a big sigh.

"Kid, is that ever going to be swell," she'll breathe in my ear, like she's giving me an inside tip on the stock market. "I saw the preview over at the Granada last week and I wouldn't miss it for nothing."

To the best of my knowledge, over the past three years,

Mildred has *yet* to see a movie that couldn't send her into at least a minor convulsion of ecstasy.

Well, you can see for yourself how easy it was to pigeon-hole Mildred. A good-hearted soul, sure, but with not too much on the ball. At least, from the neck up. It was also easy to see that, aside from pin curls and movies, her life had been—and was—a perfect vacuum. Nothing had gone deep enough to leave an imprint. Generally a person's face, by the time he's pushing forty, reflects something—for better, for worse—but Mildred's face was as bland and smooth as a china egg.

Well, last Tuesday afternoon, everything was as usual. Mildred was rubbing my scalp, Bitzi was clicking her toe-nails on the linoleum, and I was thumbing through an old *Photoplay* magazine. Suddenly Mildred reached over and pointed at a picture of Irene Dunne.

"D'ja see that movie called 'I Remember Mama'?" she demanded.

I nodded, pleased that I would be able to meet Mildred on her own grounds for a change, and then came the shocker.

"Well, I didn't like it," said Mildred flatly. "It made me start thinking."

I sat up with interest. Clearly, I had been underestimating the power of Hollywood.

"Yeah, it made me start thinking," explained Mildred, "and then the thinking made me feel bad, remembering my own Mama. I don't talk about it to my customers—naturally, you gotta *entertain* your customers—and folks don't like to listen to sad talk. But it *was* sad, just the same, when I was little. We was awful poor and there was seven of us kids, me the oldest. We had a little rented farm out in Iowa—blister-ing hot in summer, freezing cold in winter—and it was pretty mean, trying to scrape along on nothing. I can remember Mama working like a farmhand all day long and then sitting up late at night—mending and patching and knitting—so that us kids could look half-way decent. Mama was proud, she was, about appearances."

"But even if it made you feel 'bad,' " I said, somewhat unctuously, "didn't it make you feel proud, too? I mean, that you had a heroic mother like that?"

"People shouldn't have kids they can't take care of," said Mildred crisply. "Here, hand me those hairpins, will you?"

This, thought I, as I handed her the box of pins, was the time for a few well-chosen words on Divine Providence and Motherhood.

"Even when it looks that way," I said cautiously, "we humans aren't really able to judge. Big families are something to be proud of and I'll bet your sisters and brothers turned out all right, didn't they?"

"Yeah, they're doing okay," said Mildred, "but kids have got a right to a childhood. My sisters and brothers, they sure didn't have things easy, but they all got through high school. My little kid brother, he even got to State Teachers' College, what with the others helping him. But me, I was the oldest and I guess I was just the goat. You'd think, maybe, that the first child would be sorta special—maybe even spoiled—but it didn't turn out like that. Maybe it's just when the first child is a boy, I wouldn't know. Anyway, I never even had a doll—not even one made out of an old sock—and on birthdays I'd get a new pair of mittens or some hair-ribbons. And I always had to stay out of school so much and help Mama that I finally quit at the sixth grade. Mama said I was getting too big for school."

Mildred gave a short laugh. "Too big! That's a laugh, son.

After my baby was born, my husband made me go back to school and finish the eighth grade. That's a scream, ain't it? But Joe—he graduated from high school himself—said he didn't want a dumb wife, even if he did love me just the way I was. He was awful good to me, Joe was. I guess," she concluded grandly, "that I owe all that I am today to Joe."

This was my first inkling that there had been any Joe or any baby in Mildred's life but I let it pass. Things were coming too fast and my immediate concern was justice to Mama.

"Oh, but Mildred," I said righteously, "aren't you being too hard on your mother? Maybe you did have a hard childhood but, if it weren't for *her*, you wouldn't even be here."

Mildred pulled out a curl and carefully retwisted it. "What's the good of just being?" she asked. "Besides, there's some things a body just can't forget. After I married Joe, Mama disowned me. She never even came to see my baby."

"But why disowned?" Already, in the back of my mind, I felt that Mama had probably been goaded beyond her limits. Sure enough. . . .

"Oh," said Mildred airily, "we was Catholics. We come from a long line of Catholics, even got some priests in the family. Mama wouldn't let me marry Joe because he was a Methodist but Papa told me to go ahead and clear out, that I had it coming to me, that I deserved a little happiness. So I ran off and got married, I was just seventeen, before a Justice of the Peace over at Linville. Like I say, Mama was proud. She said I'd disgraced her before all the neighbors."

"But that isn't quite fair," I protested, still on the side of justice. "It wasn't just the neighbors. Why, your mother was probably broken-hearted, your leaving the Church and all."

"If you ask me," said Mildred shortly, "I wasn't leaving

nothing. I was baptized, sure, but what good does that do a
body? Mama never even let me go to church. I always had to
stay home Sunday mornings and mind the babies and clean
up the breakfast dishes and start getting the Sunday dinner.
Why, Mama, she never even let me make my First Communion."

"Oh," I said in a small voice.

"Lookie," said Mildred, "this is sad talk, isn't it? I don't
like sad talk. I don't know what got me started—oh, yes, it
was that movie. Well, I remember Mama, all right, all right."

"But sometimes you feel better," I said, "after you get
some of the sad things out of your system." I was sincere in
saying this but I was also curious as to what had happened
to Joe and the baby. I knew that Mildred and Bitzi lived
alone in a few rooms at the rear of the store. So I asked, right
out, what had happened.

Mildred didn't answer me right away. She put two wads
of cotton over my ears and adjusted the hairnet. Then, in
the mirror, our eyes met.

"You'll think this is awful silly," she said shyly, "but me
and Joe, well, you never saw two people more in love, even
if we was so poor. When I got married, and Mama disowned
me, I didn't even have a teacup to my name. Mama wouldn't
even let any of my relatives give me wedding presents because she said I was living in sin. I'll never forget the first
time we had company over for supper, me and Joe. I didn't
have no tablecloth and so what did I do but take the sheet off
the bed and starch it. Kid, that sheet turned out so stiff that
we had to sit around the table and hold it down with our
knees. Ain't that a scream?"

"But Joe and me, well, our love was just like something
in the movies. Only better, because it was real. Anyway,

maybe that's why I like movies so much, seems to bring Joe back for a little while. You know something, kid? Why, I was so crazy about that Joe that whenever I'd finish ironing one of his shirts, I'd drape the sleeves around my shoulders and pretend it was him. Hugging me hard, like he always did when he came home from work, and asking how was his little mouse. That's what he called me, little mouse. I suppose you think that's silly?"

"No-o," I said slowly, "not silly at all. But, uh, you didn't tell me what happened to him and the baby."

"Oh, Joe died," said Mildred quickly, "and then the little girl, Josephine, died four days later. She was just eight years old. They was in an accident and it seems that when Big Joe died, why, Little Joe (that's what we called them, Little Joe and Big Joe) didn't even want to get well. Those two were as thick as thieves. But I had to tell Little Joe about her daddy, she made me. I remember going into her room at the hospital that day, my eyes all red, and she said, 'Big Joe died, didn't he, Mama? You've been crying.' "

" 'You'd cry, too,' I said, real quick, 'if you'd pinched your hand like I just did in the door.' But I wasn't fooling Little Joe none. She just turned her face to the wall and wouldn't speak to me no more. So I told her. I had to, I couldn't bear her not looking at me or talking. And then she said the funniest thing for a little kid. She said, 'If Jesus wants me, it's all right now.' "

"Well, kid," said Mildred, in a sudden business-like tone, "I guess you're all ready for the drier."

The lump in my throat felt like a walnut. I couldn't say anything over that walnut and so I just got up and walked obediently over to the drier. As Mildred pulled the hood down over my head, she leaned over and shouted above the roar, "But I don't feel too bad no more. The way I see it, Little Joe is an angel, safe in heaven. Imagine me having helped make an angel. But that's what the priest told me, the day of the funeral, and I never forgot it."

This was more than I could bear. I snapped off the roar of the drier and popped my head out. "The *priest*?" I said. "Where does the priest come in?"

"Oh, why, Little Joe was a Catholic, didn't I tell you? I had her baptized right off when she was a little baby. I know it sounds crazy—me and Joe being Methodists—but that's the way I wanted it. I was bound she was going to make her First Communion. Well, she did, and she had the prettiest white veil and cutest taffeta dress you ever saw. She even had a little prayer book with a blue celluloid cover to carry in the procession."

"Mildred," said I, over that walnut in my throat, "what about yourself? You're really a Catholic yourself, you know."

"Naw," said Mildred. "I'm a Methodist like Joe. Oh, sometimes when I'm out taking Bitzi for a walk I sometimes swing around so I can go past St. Anthony's (that's where Little Joe went) but I never have the nerve to go in. You know how it is. Not ever having made my First Communion or nothing."

The raw hurt in her voice was as fresh as if it had been only yesterday.

I ducked my head back under the drier, like a turtle pulling its head back into the shell. I wanted to get away from that hurt voice because, for some funny reason, I felt almost guilty—as if I had something that didn't rightfully belong to me. Mildred could only sense her loss dimly but I—*I* could feel it for her.

Here was I, a convert, who had gained a whole new world through no merit of my own. Here also was Mildred who, through no fault of her own, had lost what rightfully belonged to her. It seemed almost unfair; it seemed almost as if, in balancing the accounts, Peter had been robbed to pay Paul. . . .

Then, for the first time in the past twenty minutes, I became aware of Bitzi: still going around and around in circles, clicking her toenails on the linoleum. How nice of Bitzi, I thought stupidly, to afford me such an immediate mortification to "offer up" for Mildred; to help readjust the accounts; to share the wealth.

But, to tell the truth, I couldn't figure out just who needed prayers the most—Methodist Mildred or her Catholic Mama.

The Milestone

IT WASN'T until they had stepped out of the elevator and started down the long dimly lit corridor that she again felt that cold wave of panic sweep over her. She glanced at the quiet little nun walking along beside her—Sister Marguerita they'd called her down at the desk—and wondered just what this Sister Marguerita would do if she suddenly dropped her overnight bag and made a dash back to the elevator. She'd make a fool of herself, of course, but she couldn't shake the feeling that she was being trapped. She was being trapped and yet here she was, putting one foot down ahead of the other and not doing a thing about it.

On the left side of the corridor was a statue, and she passed close to it. It must be St. Joseph, she thought, because she saw a carpenter's square in his hand. She noticed the chipped gilt paint on the staff he was holding and then the stiff bouquet of white gladioli at his sandaled feet. A number of small, chunky candles flickered in thick red glasses.

Back at the elevator the fear had seemed to hit her in the stomach but now it was forming into a lump in her throat. She had never been in a Catholic hospital before, and the long dim hall, those flickering red lights, and this woman, dressed in black, rustling along at her side, made her feel as if she were in a Hitchcock mystery thriller. All that was lacking was a London fog, she thought, with a detached part of her mind, but she was too frightened to be amused or even momentarily distracted by the idea.

She had to get out of here, she had to get out of here. Instead, she found herself getting farther and farther away from the elevator; she could even hear herself saying, calmly enough, over that lump in her throat, that no, the bag wasn't heavy and that yes, it certainly was warming up outside. Yet how could her voice be saying all this when she wanted really to shout out ridiculous things like: I can't go through with this, I'm too scared, you can't expect me to have a baby all alone like this!

There was absolutely no alternative and so it was absurd, of course, but still this way there seemed to be nothing natural or immediate about it. There was just the operation tomorrow morning at eight. Eight o'clock was practically dawn, wasn't it? *The General Died At Dawn*, starring Gary Cooper and Madeleine Carroll. . . .

She began to feel too hot in her fur coat and rubber galoshes.

They stopped at room 318, and she stood there in the doorway as Sister Marguerita went on into the room. She crossed the room and quickly raised the window shade, then turned and beckoned for the girl to come on in. "Here, dear," she said in her whispering, paper-dry voice, "put your bag down and sit in this rocker until the nurse can come to take care of you." She patted the back of the big oak rocking chair and smiled at her kindly, the smile breaking her wrinkled face into a thousand little creases. "And what would you like, dear, a boy or a girl?"

The girl sat down heavily in the stiff, clumsy rocker, her eyes never leaving the nun's face. It was like having the grocer say, "And what'll you have, lady, the drip grind or the regular?"

"It doesn't matter," she said shortly. "It won't keep my husband out of the war and so what difference does it make, whether it's a boy or girl?"

The nun looked rather shocked. She reached over and patted the girl's shoulder. "You're upset, dear. You've been sick, haven't you? You just sit still and rest, dear, and I'll go after the nurse." Her skirts swished dryly as she moved toward the door and out into the corridor.

Alone, the girl sat staring moodily at the smoke-tan walls, the heavy varnished dresser, the high narrow bed, as yet unmade. In a corner the radiator spat and dripped; her feet felt hot and constricted in the rubber galoshes. She reached over and unsnapped the top button but she couldn't quite manage the rest of them. Then she took off her coat and draped it over the end of the bed, first fishing around in the pocket for her cigarettes. Cigarettes really didn't appeal to her much these days, but right now smoking would at least be something to do. The room was so ugly and impersonal there in the flood of pale, watery sunlight that it gave her an unnerving sense of unreality. Was someone she knew going to climb into that bed?

She looked around for an ashtray and then got up and walked over to the dresser. She pulled open the drawer on the left and looked inside. It was lined with a clean newspaper and in it were a small enameled pan for brushing teeth, a roll of cotton in blue paper, and some scattered toothpicks. She picked up the enameled pan and walked with it over to the window where she put it down on the wide window ledge. In the afternoon sunshine she could see the gleaming top of the First Loan and Trust Building, or at least she guessed that was the building. She'd only been in the town a month and hadn't got her bearings yet. I'm a stranger here myself, she thought with that detached part of her mind that kept thinking up funny things that just weren't funny.

Standing there in the full light, her mouth looked hard because she had drawn on the lipstick with a savage flourish. But everything else about her was defenseless and young-looking. Her short light brown hair was brushed into soft curls; her eyes were blue with large black pupils.

She tapped out her cigarette ash in the toothbrush pan, noticing at the same time what a smooth job she'd done on her fingernails. It was this new red shade called "Bravo." Bravo, bravo, bravo.

Yes, Mrs. Joubert, the doctor had said (only yesterday), you're going to be perfectly all right. It's just that you've got this toxemia and we'd better play safe and make this a Caesarian baby. Since your husband isn't here to give his consent, should we ask your husband's aunt? Is she your closest relative around here?

(Sure, ask Aunt Ruth. She's a very close relative. I've known her a whole month now. And they say the new ruling is that your only visitors can be your husband and mother. With your husband in the Navy and your mother in California, that just about leaves the field to Aunt Ruth, doesn't it? Aunt Ruth, who works at the plant all night and sleeps all day.)

If only she could take a pill to dissolve that lump in her throat. She was frightened but aside from her fear was the deep disappointment inside her. Her first baby, and nothing was like she'd ever dreamed it would be. Other women and their husbands rushed to the hospital together; they were excited, they were flustered, they did funny things they laughed over later. Then the husband paced the floor of the waiting room, leaving cigarette stub after cigarette stub on the linoleum floor. Then it was all over and the father rushed to the phone and dropped nickel after nickel into the slot. The mother sat up the next day, a ribbon around her head, and opened telegrams and daintily plucked cards from between the cool green stems of roses. And there was always at least one pottery baby shoe filled with babies'-breath and rosebuds and sweet peas.

Oh, she knew all right what it was supposed to be like. Two of her best friends, back there in California, had gone through the same thing. It was all a standard pattern. It was supposed to be a milestone in your life.

Suddenly the bright top of the First Loan and Trust Building began to blur and she knew that she was going to cry at last. There was a miserable satisfaction in feeling the first tears spill over although it made that lump in her throat feel even worse.

When the nurse walked briskly into the room, fresh sheets on her arm, it startled her so that she bumped her ankle against the radiator as she turned around.

"Don't you believe in knocking around here?" The girl said it so sharply that her breath came in with a little hiss.

The nurse was a thin, washed-out blonde of around thirty-five. Her pale eyes were red around the edges and she looked as if she needed sleep badly.

She stared at the girl for a full second and then said, in a flat, even voice, "We certainly do *not* knock around here."

She laid the clean sheets on the bed and then hung up the fur coat, ignoring the galoshes still on the girl's feet. Quickly and efficiently, she started to unpack the suitcase. Slippers by the bed, the bathrobe in the closet, the bedjackets in the lower dresser drawer.

The girl sat down in the rocker and watched the nurse as she started to make the bed. She was so angry that she was almost shaking, and because of her anger the tears had stopped as quickly as they had started.

The nurse pulled the sheets across as tight and straight as a board and deftly turned the corners. As she flipped open the folded blue cotton blanket, she glanced up and said, "Well, we've stopped crying. That's good. Now we'll feel better."

The black pupils in the girl's eyes seemed to shrink to a pinhole. "You—you cold potato, you," she said slowly. "You're certainly a model Florence Nightingale, aren't you?" She wanted to be deadly sarcastic but she sounded young and ineffectual even to her own ears.

The nurse gave the pillow a smart pat. "As a matter of fact, I *am* a pretty good nurse," she said. "But listen, what were you crying about? You feel all right, don't you?"

The girl started to tell her but the first thing she knew she was crying again and it was coming out all mixed up. She finished off lamely, her voice ending in a squeak that made her furious, "And I can't—I can't unsnap the rest of my galoshes."

The nurse knelt down before her and started to take them off. With her head averted, and her voice low, she said, "You're just a kid, aren't you? I didn't intend to sound so mean but I'm awfully tired. Just too many babies around here, I guess. But I'd like to tell you something that might make you feel differently."

The girl stiffened. "If you're going to talk about patriotism and courage and all that sort of . . ."

"No, I'm not," said the nurse, her head still averted. "It's about me and I probably wouldn't be telling you if I weren't so blamed tired. It's just that—well, yesterday morning I found out that the man I was engaged to had been killed. In Korea."

The girl stared at her. "Gee, that's terrible," she said awkwardly. "I'm awfully sorry."

The nurse straightened up and walked over to the closet with the galoshes. "Thanks," she said briefly. "They told me I could take a couple of days off but they had to call me back last night. Too many babies. But I'm going to be all right. It's just that when you turned around at the window and I saw how young and pretty you were, I couldn't help feeling jealous and, well, angry for a minute. To think you were crying because you were going to have a baby while I could cry because I never will."

"But how do you," began the girl, timidly, "I mean, I don't see . . ."

"Oh, yes, you *can* see," said the nurse, turning an unbecoming red. "I'm no glamor girl and I'm no spring chicken. He was the only beau I ever had. Well," she cleared her throat abruptly. "I'll be back in a few minutes. I got another light on down the hall."

The girl watched her disappear around the corner of the doorway and then turned her head to look out the window. Sitting down like that, she could see only the gray-blue sky and the tips of a few bare trees. Pretty soon she began to rock slowly back and forth.

When the nurse returned she had a hospital nightgown of natural-colored sacking over one arm. "Well," she said, with an impersonal smile as if they'd never met before, "and what do you want, a boy or a girl?"

"Oh, I don't know," the girl said slowly, as if she were thinking it over for the first time, "a girl, I guess. I think a little girl would be more fun to dress and take care of, don't you?"

Her voice sounded faraway and rather complacent.

The Little Girls

I T WAS the little girls that made it so hard. Even though they remembered to whisper (actually, they were as good as gold), they were the ones who made it so hard for the mother. Maybe it was because of their freshly scrubbed faces, trying hard to be solemn but showing only a frank, bright interest. Most of them had never seen a dead person before.

There were nine of the little girls and, in their light summer dresses, they looked like a bevy of small white moths as they clustered around her daughter.

"My," whispered one of the little girls, "don't she look *natural*?" She wasn't quite sure what the word meant, but she had heard one of the older people say it. "Just as *natural*," she repeated. She reached out and furtively touched the tufted white plush of the casket. It seemed funny to think that this was really Mary Ellen.

In the school plays she had always had the choice roles (the Christmas Spirit, the Snow Queen, the Sugar Plum Princess) because she was easily the prettiest girl in the fourth grade. The other little girls—the ones with freckles, unsuccessful home permanents, and big front teeth—simply

213

took this for granted. They even boasted about her. She could act as well as had Margaret O'Brien, at her age, and she was ten times prettier. They hadn't a doubt in the world but that she was going to end up in Hollywood.

She always looked wonderful in the dyed cheesecloth costumes that the nuns concocted, and now the little girls were disappointed to see that Mary Ellen had on her Sunday best dress: the blue rayon one, princess style, with the yarn flowers on the pockets. They had vaguely expected something more dramatic, maybe something white and flowing like the Snow Queen's costume. They also regretted the curls.

Generally Mary Ellen wore her hair in long smooth curls but, during the summer vacation, her mother always braided it because it was cooler. Now it was July, and so there were braids. It was really too bad, thought the little girls, because braids were so old-fashioned.

"Just think," whispered one of the little girls. "She got a stomach-ache on Monday and died on Wednesday."

"*I* know it," said the girl next to her. "I knew about it before *you* did. My mother was the one who called people about the flowers." For the third time, she crossed herself. Carefully and importantly. But she crossed herself because it seemed proper, not to ward off any future stomach-aches of her own.

Sudden death did not even seem to brush the little girls. Their fearful mothers had insulated them against fear; their worried mothers (remembering the tears shed over the bullet-torn fawn in *The Yearling*) had talked only about the beautiful death.

("See, honey, they operated on Mary Ellen and she just never woke up again, she kept right on sleeping. Wasn't that a *nice* way to die? And now she's so *happy*.")

The mothers need not have worried. The Technicolor make-believe death of the yearling was one thing, the death of a classmate another. The little girls didn't get good grades in Christian Doctrine for nothing. They had it reduced to the bone. The saints were the lucky ones. Mary Ellen was in heaven. You couldn't get into heaven unless you were a saint. Therefore, lucky.

The odd thing was that Sister Agatha, the one who taught Christian Doctrine, was crying like anything. Her face, generally like smooth marble, was all crumpled up. The little girls nudged each other. Sister Agatha—did you see Sister *Agatha?*

But the little girls themselves, Mary Ellen's closest friends, felt only a lively interest, a certain shared pride in her latest achievement. She had always been two jumps ahead of them, anyway—the prettiest, the quickest, the brightest—and this time *they* shared in the winnings. The parish priest, not slowed down by red tape in Rome, had said that now their new school had a child saint all its own to pray to.

Last year their school had won the Fire Prevention Certificate and the city softball championship. St. Michael's School was doing all right for itself.

The mother stood at one end of the white casket, the father at the other. This had been their only child, a child of their middle years. Somehow, they managed to recognize the faces, remember the names of the people who filed along in a steady line: the mothers of the little girls, neighbors and relatives, the nuns from the school. They were the grown-ups, and grief flowed through the steady line as from a common wound.

But it was the little girls who made it so hard. The mother could not help being aware of the little girls, brushing against her, whispering importantly. They represented an official body, standing guard as chief mourners. They were all members of the Busy Bee Blue Bird group—fledgling Camp Fire Girls—and Mary Ellen had been their president.

During the year the Busy Bees had sold doughnuts in the Doughnut Drive, gone on nature hikes, learned songs with motions, made pan holders for Mother's Day. Like every stalwart organization, they even had a Way of Life. It was called "The Blue Bird Wish" and it was pasted on the front page of every good Busy Bee's notebook:

To have fun.

To learn to make beautiful things.

To remember to finish what I begin.

To want to keep my temper.

To go to interesting places.

To learn about trees, flowers, and birds.

To make friends.

There were so many new things to learn, so many interesting places to go. During the past school year their leader had taken them to visit the interesting places: the radio station, the city hall, the bakery, the airport, the dairy. Now, in their bright summer dresses, they were visiting a funeral home.

The last time the mother had seen them they had been wearing bright blue shorts and white shirts. Two weeks ago they had had a picnic at Colfax Park and Mary Ellen's father and mother had gone along as sponsors. There had been roasted wienies, marshmallows, popsicles, singing, throwing stones in the river. It was almost, said the little girls on the way home, as good as going to camp. Maybe better. They liked to talk big about camp but didn't want it much closer. When you went to camp you didn't get to see your folks for a whole ten days.

All the way home, crammed into the battered old Buick, they had sung their songs. They were too crowded to sing the funny ones with motions, like the one about the eensy, weensy spider going up the water spout, but there were plenty of others. Over and over, they had sung the official song of the Blue Birds because that was the one you sang at ceremonial meetings:

> Pretty little Blue Bird, why do you go?
> Come back, come back to me;
> I go, said the bird as he flew on high,
> To see if my color matches the sky.

It was an awfully pretty song except, sometimes, they got it started too high. Then they would end up on a high squeak and a giggle, like they did with "The Star-Spangled Banner."

The line had thinned out, and there were only a few more hands for the parents to shake. In one corner of the vestibule a fourth grade mother was busily checking names and donations with other fourth grade mothers. Theirs was the huge spray of lilies and larkspur. They had finally decided on flowers, after a certain amount of liturgical confusion as to what was proper. It didn't seem quite right to give Spiritual Bouquets for a little girl who really didn't need them.

The rest of the grownups had gone back into the other parlor or drifted out onto the porch to wait for the priest. The July night was warm and still. When the priest came, at eight o'clock, there would be the Rosary.

But the little girls stayed, playing guard at the casket, not giving up their rightful ground. Over their whispering and bobbing heads the parents glanced at each other, sharing the mixed and peculiar pain. The little girls were whispering, all right, but they could hear every word.

"What's her name in heaven?" one of them was saying. "Is she called Saint Mary?"

Then she frowned, puzzled. "But there're so many Marys, mightn't they get mixed up?" It was always that way. Even in the classroom there were always too many Marys. She wanted no confusion about the one from St. Michael's.

A newcomer, a late Busy Bee, joined the ranks. She looked warm and breathless, as if she had been running.

"Did you register in the book?" one of them whispered officiously. The newcomer, still breathless, shook her head dumbly, and the officious one whisked her off. The mother, her face swollen with grief, watched them as they darted out into the vestibule to register proudly another Busy Bee.

They're little, she told herself, they don't realize. The little girls seemed heartless but her own daughter might have acted the same way. It might have been Mary Ellen darting out into the vestibule like that. She knew all about little girls. Maybe it was even unfair to think they were heartless; they had hearts, all right, but they were children's hearts. They could believe whatever anyone told them.

The mother had been told a number of things, too, these past sixteen hours. The old phrases had dashed against her tired mind and then fallen away: "Time heals all wounds—God's ways are inscrutable—Thy will be done—God fits the burden to the back—The Lord giveth and the Lord taketh away. . . ."

She had grown up with these phrases, heard them all her life. They were part of her very blood stream. Maybe later, when she wasn't so tired, the meaning and the sense would creep back into them.

"How God must have loved you," the priest had said gently, "to give you so heavy a cross to bear." But her mind was too heavy, too tired for the paradox. Her mind could only circle back, again and again, to the simple beginning. It was Monday noon—Mary Ellen had come in from jumping rope to say she had a stomach-ache—but kids were always having little stomach-aches . . .

It was a merciful relief when the Rosary began and the mother could get down on her knees. She was so tired that she rested one elbow on the seat of the folding chair next to her. Her feet throbbed; she had been on them almost constantly since Monday. But it was odd, since she ached all over, that she should even think of her feet.

The little girls had quit whispering, were kneeling around her, were busily untangling their small colored beads. Now there was just the priest leading the prayers: the Hail Marys tumbling out like water rushing over worn smooth stones. This, too, seemed almost senseless. And yet between the decades was a strange new line that the mother had never heard before: "May she rejoice with the angels and the saints forever." "May she rejoice . . ."

It was a beautiful death, they said. And tomorrow at the funeral there would be the Mass of the Angels. Oh, she had much to be grateful for—they were right, this *was* a beautiful death—and there had been mothers far less lucky . . .

The Mass of the Angels. That meant that tomorrow there would be no black in the church because black stood for mourning. The priest would wear white vestments, symbol of innocence and joy, and flowers would be permitted (the fourth grade mothers had sent such a lovely spray) because it was a time for rejoicing. Like a feast day.

For a moment, she let bitterness spurt up in her heart

unchecked. *They* had their saint, but she had no daughter.
Let the priest wear his white. Let the little girls wear their
bright summer dresses. *She* would wear black, she would
wear black forever. . . .

But she could not even hold onto a sustained bitterness. It
was alien to her; it wasn't part of her blood stream. Like all
the other phrases these, too, dashed against her tired mind
and then fell away.

The Rosary was over quickly, like everything else had
been going these past sixteen hours. The mother got up from
her knees, stiffly and clumsily, but the little girls scrambled
to their feet with ease. It was as if they had elastic in their
joints. Even when a child broke a leg or a collarbone, the
young bones started mending and healing immediately.
Elastic.

Her eyes followed them as they wandered out into the
vestibule to wait for their mothers to join them. For a few
more days, she thought dully, the little girls would still talk
about the beautiful death and then there would be new interests to absorb them. By next fall, when school opened,
Mary Ellen would be only a . . .

But one of the little girls seemed to be hanging back, the
little girl who had come in late and breathless. She seemed
undecided about something and then, with sudden resolution,
she walked over to the mother.

"Mama said I shouldn't give it to you," she said with a
little rush, "because Mary Ellen didn't need a Spiritual
Bouquet, but I'd already made it and so—well, and so here it
is." She thrust a folded piece of manila paper into the
mother's hands and, turning, walked swiftly away.

The mother opened the paper. At the top, in heavy black
crayola, was a big "J.M.J." Underneath, in uneven printing,

it said: "I will say 1,000 Hail Marys for Mary Ellen Dunlap. Signed, her friend Helen Jo Mackey." Then, this time in purple crayola, was a row of crosses, followed by a P.S. "I will never forget her as long as I live."

The mother folded the paper carefully. It seemed to make even her tonsils ache, for she knew all about little girls. She had seen extravagant homemade Spiritual Bouquets before. She knew exactly how much they could mean and yet, somehow, this was the nicest one she had ever seen. *I will never forget her as long as I live. . .*

She turned to her husband and handed him the slip of paper without a word. Maybe it would make him feel better, too.

Elizabeth

MAYBE IT was the casual tweed suit and blue bow tie that bothered her. She was used to seeing him in his white starched jacket, and in the tweed suit he might have been almost anyone: a golf pro, a real estate agent, a band leader, a mailman on his day off . . .

"Doctor!" she said urgently. He was almost out to the corridor. "Wait a minute!"

He half turned, resting a big hand on the doorway, waiting for her to go on.

"Doctor," she began, and then she stopped. She hadn't intended her "Wait a minute!" to sound so urgent, so imperative, and now her question would stick out like a sore thumb. Doctors didn't like to be pinned down, they didn't like their patients to. . .

"Doctor," she began again, not looking at him, "this is a funny question but I—well, I was just wondering about the chances. I mean, that something might go wrong tomorrow morning."

"Hey," he said, walking back to the bed. "What'd you mean by *chances?*"

He turned to the nurse who was making the hospital rounds with him, spreading his hands in a helpless gesture. "Did you hear what I heard?" he asked. " 'Chances,' the lady says. Should I sue her for slander?"

The nurse giggled. It was always fun making the rounds with Doctor Higglethorne; he had such a perfectly marvellous sense of humor.

Now he reached over and wiggled Elizabeth's foot under the thin cotton blanket. "Look," he said, "if you weren't supposed to be sick, I'd give you a good paddling. You don't look much older than a twelve-year-old, at that, with that pony tail you're wearing. But *chances*!"

Suddenly he thrust out his underlip, scowling fiercely, and drawled: "When you make dirty cracks like that, partner, you—*smile*."

The nurse tittered and so Elizabeth smiled too, feeling foolish. The horseplay embarrassed her and she was sorry now that she had called him back. The operation, to him, was probably no more exciting than swabbing a skinned knee with mercurochrome. And it wasn't his fault, exactly, that a tweed suit wasn't as reassuring as a white uniform or that he didn't act like young Dr. Kildare in the movies.

"Well," she said lamely, "I just thought I'd ask. It's at— uh—eight o'clock, you said?"

"Eight o'clock," he repeated heartily, his face again wreathed in smiles. Everything was fixed up. It might have been a date to play tennis.

It wasn't until he had gone on down the corridor that Elizabeth remembered that he hadn't, exactly, answered her question.

When the nurse brought in the evening paper, at six-thirty, she tried it again. Only, this time she was clever. "Oh, nurse,"

she said, as if it were just an afterthought. "I wonder if
you'd do me a favor. They're operating tomorrow, you know,
and I probably won't feel like reading the papers for a few
days. Would you mind saving them for me?"

She watched the nurse's face closely, looking for a tell-
tale flicker, an off-guard reaction. ("Oh, my poor lamb, *you*
won't be reading any more papers. Didn't you *know*?")

"Sure thing," said the nurse pleasantly. Her face was as
smooth and non-committal as a hard-boiled egg. "I'll put
them in the upper right hand dresser drawer for you. How
would that be? I know how it is, missing a few days, especially with the comics."

She bent over to crank up the bed. "Would you like it
higher?" she asked.

"Thanks," said Elizabeth.

Alone, she flipped open the paper and started to read.
Damn them, she thought, damn them. If they were in her
shoes, they wouldn't be so damned egg-faced. And she had
a right to know about chances, she had a right to a straight
answer. She didn't want them just to wiggle her foot or roll
up the bed.

Even a gangster, she thought angrily, got fairer treatment.
What was it they always said in the Grade C movies? Oh yes,
"You're going for a ride, buddy, and you ain't coming back.
Better pray fast, bud."

With a gun at your back, you'd *know*. You'd have a little
warning, you'd make every minute count. There would be
none of this shilly-shallying: feeling scared one minute and
then feeling foolish the next.

Because it *was* foolish, of course. Doctors did anything
and everything nowadays. Why, only last month she had
taken her cocker spaniel to one of those swanky dog hospitals

for a rabies shot. The veterinarian had taken her into the operating room where an English bulldog was having a gall bladder operation, just as neat as you please. It was really wonderful the way Science was—the way Science had. . . .

Elizabeth put down the paper she wasn't reading. She knew she didn't give a hoot about that English bulldog. Her stomach felt as if it were packed in dry ice.

I'm scared, she thought, I'm scared to pieces, but it's a perfectly normal reaction. It doesn't mean a thing, I'm even scared of a dentist. And everyone must feel this way, the night before a major operation. Naturally, I'm a little nervous— *naturally.* . . .

It was just that—well, if she could just talk about it. If there was just someone—someone who didn't matter, someone she'd never see again—that she could talk to. Maybe like Roman Catholics went to a priest. It seemed rather silly, talking in the dark to a man who didn't know you, but it was probably good psychology.

Once she had tried to ask Walter about it (she had really wanted to know) but he had shut up like a clam. It was before they were married and he had just reached over and patted her hand. "I'm afraid I couldn't explain it right to you, sweetheart," he had said, "and it would just sound funny. You'd think me a queer duck, following a religion that would seem strange to you, but you don't have to worry, honest. I mean, I promise I won't ever bring up my religion. It won't make a speck of difference between us."

He had kept his promise, too. He'd really been very nice and decent about it. He had always said that religion was a private concern and that he loved her too much to inflict his beliefs upon her.

Yes, she appreciated it—lots of Catholics would have been

narrow-minded—but, in a way, it was sort of a joke. Walter, so afraid of creating a barrier between them; Walter, having so much respect for her private beliefs. What beliefs?

Elizabeth turned on her side, doubling the pillow under her head. You could pack all her beliefs into a thimble but, anyway, that was neither here nor there. All she wanted, right now, was someone to talk to. Any size, shape, age, or color. Even the hospital janitor would do.

If the janitor could just come in and sit down for a while. She could say, "You know, I feel so funny. It's really pretty important, not knowing for sure if I'm going to be alive tomorrow or not, but it's against the rules to talk about chances. It's not civilized, not good etiquette, not being a good sport. People die every day but you're not supposed to notice it. I guess it's something like B.O. or five o'clock shadow. Would *you* mind talking. . . ."

No, the janitor wouldn't be any good, she could tell that already. "There's some dame in room 215," he'd say on his way back to the boiler room, "that about talked a leg off me. Crazy as a hoot owl."

But maybe what she needed, for peace of mind, wasn't the janitor but a lawyer. A lawyer would understand how it was, this urge to clear up loose ends. If something went wrong tomorrow, why—why, it would be like sneaking out the back door, leaving the dishes unwashed, everything in disorder, saying nothing to anyone. It wasn't efficient.

But a lawyer understood efficiency and she could say to him, with no nonsense and even a touch of nobility: "Well, now, jot this down, please. You're to tell my husband (naturally, I can't) that in the event of my decease, I want him to remarry. In—in, oh, about three years, maybe. He loves me very much, you understand, but I really think it would be better if he. . . ."

Elizabeth rolled over on her stomach and wept. Being efficient made her feel even worse. And it was no good being tough, no good thinking, "C'mon, do you want to live *forever*?" She guessed she did. Maybe it would be different if she were old and withering on the vine but she was only twenty-seven. She didn't even feel particularly sick. If it hadn't been for that old X-ray. . . .

Elizabeth sat up, reached over to the end table, yanked out a piece of Kleenex, and blew her nose. Then she crumpled the Kleenex into a tight little ball and aimed it at the metal wastebasket over by the dresser. It missed, rolling under the radiator.

She was going to be perfectly all right. Doctors did anything and everything nowadays. All she asked, she thought coldly, was not to be left alone beforehand. All she wanted was a stooge, a human prop of some sort, to talk to. Yet she'd tried the doctor, the nurse, the janitor, the lawyer—who was left?

One thing was certain. "Husband" was out.

She remembered reading somewhere that if everyone were given just five more minutes to live, the phone booths all over the nation would be jammed with people telling other people how much they loved them. Maybe so. But this was precisely what you couldn't say when you and your husband were both pretending that nothing could possibly go wrong. It would sound like a farewell speech; they would scare each other.

Take this afternoon: visiting hours from two to four. Since Walter couldn't come back this evening, it was possible—not probable, possible—that those were their last hours together.

Yet they might well have been their first hours. It was like an embarrassed first date: straining for safe topics, painfully conscious of the awkward pauses, stringing out the small talk.

Around three o'clock he had become so jittery he had dashed out to the corner drugstore and brought back two malteds and a movie magazine. The malteds, sipped slowly, had killed another fifteen minutes.

But what had they talked about? She couldn't even remember. All she could remember was his exit. He had kissed her goodbye, lightly, and mumbled something about chin up and not to take any wooden nickels. Poor Walter. He loved her so much.

It was beginning to look very much as if this were a lonely business. *Afterwards*, when it was all over, there would be all sorts of people streaming in: all solicitude, all cheer, all bearing gifts of flowers and comic "Get well fast, you hear?" greeting cards. *Afterwards*, there would be the corporal works of mercy.

She guessed she wasn't very brave but, still, she bet there were lots of other people in the hospital, right this minute, as mixed-up and lonely and scared as herself. The misery loves company idea seemed to help a little, to take away some of the loneliness. When you thought of yourself as part of a group, it wasn't so bad. In groups, people were even heroic—like in war or in sudden disasters and stuff.

Like in that book she had pored over, as a kid, called *The Sinking of the Titanic*. It had really happened; there were actual photos to prove it. Everyone had been dancing or playing cards and, suddenly, they had hit this iceberg and started sinking. No hope. The band had started playing "Nearer, My God, to Thee" and everyone had stood on the deck singing. Husbands and wives had clung to each other, still singing (like a Kathryn Grayson–Howard Keel close-up in the movies) as the water reached their feet. Everyone had been tremendously brave, tremendously.

Now she began to wonder. Did that author know how brave they were when they began to sink separately? *Even in someone's arms you would still be alone, terribly alone.* It wouldn't matter who was with you—doctor, lawyer, janitor, husband—you would still be alone.

The thought hit her like a blow in the stomach. Alone, you would not be Walter's wife but—just Elizabeth. And she'd never paid very much attention to Elizabeth.

Don't think, she said to herself, don't think. Doctor Higglethorne was right, after all, in not giving her a straight answer. Only a saint could bear a straight answer and she, Elizabeth, didn't even want to *think* about chances.

She reached over to the end table, shoved aside the box of Kleenex, and picked up the movie magazine that Walter had brought her. Love sends a little gift of the latest *Photoplay*, she thought, over the dry ice in her stomach, and then felt a stab of compunction. Walter loved her very much. She knew he did. It had been very nice and considerate of him to think about the magazine; it would help her to keep her mind off—off *things*.

She opened the *Photoplay* at random and stared down at the glossy smile of Betty Grable.

The Mouse Hunter

WHEN FATHER MACKEY (class of '41) had become a priest according to the order of Melchisedech forever, he had been prepared—nay, eager—to die for his Faith at a moment's notice. But this form of *slow* death, right in one's own rectory parlor, was something else again. With something akin to pure envy, he found himself thinking of his classmates who had chosen the primrose path: the foreign missions, where one faced only bullets, jungle rot, boa constrictors. . . .

"And this tablecloth," Mrs. Dalrymple was saying, "took five solid months to crochet, not to mention the strain on my eyes using number eighty ecru thread. It's the shell pattern —always tasty, don't you think, Father?—and the tickets should sell like hot cakes. Now, Father, I'm more than willing to donate my handiwork, not to mention the strain on my eyes using number eighty thread, but I *must* insist on cooperation. At our last bazaar, if you'll remember," and here she fixed him with the glittering eye of the Ancient Mariner, "you not only forgot to get the tickets printed on time but had them printed wrong. The Sanctuary ladies had to waste one whole afternoon scratching out 'bedspread' and writing in 'afghan.'"

Father Mackey smiled a smile that he hoped betrayed an appealing and helpless boyishness. "But I thought an afghan *was* a sort of bedspread," he said, "and the spelling was certainly easier."

"Humph," said Mrs. Dalrymple, riding roughshod over the boyish charm. "Moreover, I think it only fair and decent that the tickets be printed 'Beautiful handmade ecru tablecloth, donated by Mrs. Clarence F. Dalrymple.' Perhaps you'd better jot that down, Father."

Mrs. Clarence F. Dalrymple had *not* built St. Anthony's Church single-handed, brick by brick, but she was easily equivalent, in power, to the flying buttresses that held up its roof. And if she considered her crocheting on a par with a stained glass window, there was nothing to do but make the proper dedication.

Father Mackey groped unhappily in his pockets for a piece of scrap paper and came up with the two letters that had arrived in the morning mail. One was from his classmate Joe Givern, now a missionary out on the Gold Coast (oh, primrose path—oh, jungle rot and boa constrictors), and he hastily stuffed it back in his pocket.

The other letter, with its familiar cellophane window, was from the Berg and Berg Plumbing Supply Company for the sum of $15.67 for repairing the boys' toilet. At the last Cub Scout meeting, young Tony Hammerschmidt—on a double dare from Butch Armstrong—had tried to flush down several blackboard erasers.

As Father Mackey scribbled "beautiful ecru tablecloth" on the back of the plumbing bill, he wondered uneasily if Mrs. Dalrymple had heard of the episode. If so, there would be the devil to pay. She would be satisfied with nothing less than the electric chair for young Hammerschmidt.

"And now, Father," continued Mrs. Dalrymple, "let's settle this unpleasant business about the health board." Her last attack of asthma, her scruples over hiring a Baptist cleaning woman, her latest bitter conflict with Sister Carmelita, and her ecru tablecloth had been disposed of, but Father Mackey —with dispirited insight—knew that they had only reached the fifth station. The Way of the Cross continued.

"Miss Cronk has been working in the kitchen for the past ten years, fixing the school lunches, and never before has anyone questioned the purity of her blood. She says she wouldn't so much mind being vaccinated or being asked to wear a hairnet in the kitchen, but to submit to a Wassermann test, *no*. Now, Father, I thought if you would just see the Bishop and explain to him that Miss Cronk is a monthly communicant and the vice-president of the Children of Mary, you could easily get a dispensation."

Father Mackey had met the Bishop but once (on that dreadful day of Confirmation when Ralphie Plunkett, with his nervous stomach, had been sick at the Bishop's feet) and did not crave a further audience.

"I'm sure I can swing Miss Cronk around to the health board's point of view," he now said, with a certain masterfulness born of necessity, and indeed he really thought he could. Miss Cronk, if unduly sensitive about the purity of her blood, was also piously responsive. He would bring up the Presentation in the Temple and he felt quite sure—if he heavily stressed the parallel between the humility of the Virgin Mary and that of Miss Cronk—that all would be well.

Mrs. Dalrymple gave a little sniff of open skepticism. Perhaps Father *thought* he had Miss Cronk in the hollow of his hand, but Father could just think again. Miss Cronk's allegiance, like everyone else's, was still with the former pastor, God rest his soul, who had been a living saint, God rest his soul. More important, he had even *looked* like a saint, with his sad refined-looking face and his tall spare figure and his crest of silver hair.

But this Father Mackey! Standing before the altar of God at Mass, he simply looked like a third altar boy. Shouldn't a priest be required to *look* like a priest? Be selected with the same liturgical care as, say, a new baptismal font? A *minimum* requirement for seminarians, Mrs. Dalrymple felt, was that they at least be six feet tall, so as to get the full decorative value out of the vestments that the Sanctuary ladies so carefully tended.

Even worse than his stature (and Mrs. Dalrymple would have regarded as pure heresy the fact that St. Paul was a little squirt of a man) was the growing suspicion that Father Mackey was a *radical*. Only a radical would let a smelly old tramp sleep on a cot in the church basement (pretending he was a watchman!) or let the Protestant kids use the playground after school or talk about racial justice or keep a housekeeper who . . .

Mrs. Dalrymple settled herself a little more firmly into the old Morris chair and Father Mackey, noticing the settling, felt a sense of inner strangulation. Somewhere along the line, his seminarian training had failed him. It had provided tiresome hours of rubric and dogma instead of a brisk practical course on how to propel, firmly yet graciously, females like Mrs. Dalrymple to the front door.

An hour ago, he had been prepared to embrace her, so to speak, but by now his joy in expiation was wearing thin. It was an article of faith that God would not try a man beyond his strength; but, tonight, it did seem as if God were stretching things. Generally, his evenings—especially when he was try-

ing to give convert instructions—were punctured with untimely phone calls but, tonight, there was only a deadly
calm. He and the Ancient Mariner were adrift on a painted
sea, with nary a breeze in the offing.

As Mrs. Dalrymple launched into a report on the cracked
window shades in the fourth grade room, he found himself
wishing that a mouse might suddenly streak across the room.
The rectory was full of mice. Couldn't just *one* little fellow
obligingly dart in Mrs. Dalrymple's direction, please? But,
no, she would probably just step on the poor creature, with
one crunch of her corrective shoes, and go right on talking.
No, it would take something far more spectacular to deliver
him—fire, flood, earthquake. . . .

Ah, perhaps the sudden crash of an automobile collision in
front of the rectory so that he could rush out, trampling
over Mrs. Dalrymple, to administer Extreme Unction. Master-
fully pushing his way through the crowd, he—little Father
Mackey—would fearlessly drag the victim from the burning
car and kneel over him, oblivious to the second-degree burns
on his own hands and face.

"That's Father Mackey, the new paster of St. Anthony's,"
the bystanders would murmur in awed whispers. "Man alive,
he's as plucky as they come."

Father (Walter Mitty) Mackey, the plucky new pastor of St.
Anthony's, gave himself a disgusted little shake—"Far off let
idle visions fly, no phantom of the night molest"—and came
back to the hard realities.

"I'm sorry, Mrs. Dalrymple," he said. "I'm afraid I lost
the thread of our interesting discussion. You were saying
something about cracked window shades?"

To his surprise, a dull wave of red crawled up Mrs.
Dalrymple's cheeks. "Your housekeeper," she blurted. "I—

we—that is, the ladies insisted I speak to you about it. Surely, Father, you aren't letting her stay on?"

So here it was. The hard realities. Father Mackey found himself cracking his knuckles, as he had used to crack them, from nervousness, during his oral exams. Only this time, along with the nervousness, he felt a certain breathless abandonment such as Joan of Arc might have felt as they touched the first burning taper to the straw.

"You mean because she's pregnant?" he asked, and watched, with a peculiar fascination, the wave of red crawl right up under Mrs. Dalrymple's black felt hat. It was almost a temptation to say the word *pregnant* again. Instead, he continued obtusely, "But I think it's splendid, don't you? She and Jim have wanted a baby for so long."

He could still see Rose, standing in the kitchen doorway, twisting one corner of her apron, as she had made the glad and fearful annunciation.

"I see no point," he went on, savoring the unprecedented miracle of a Mrs. Dalrymple struck speechless, "in firing a perfectly good housekeeper just because God has seen fit to let her become a mother. Do you?"

Mrs. Dalrymple opened her mouth like a goldfish. "But, *Father*," she said. "A *baby*. A baby in the *rectory*."

Father Mackey gave a little shrug. "As a priest," he said mildly, "I can hardly insist that my housekeeper practice birth control."

Mrs. Dalrymple, this time like a dying goldfish, gave a little gasp and Father Mackey half-expected to see her rise to the top of the bowl and float on her side. Instead, with a sudden flip of its tail, the goldfish came to life.

With unbearable suspense, he saw that she was actually heaving to her feet; was actually heading toward the door.

Never in the annals of St. Anthony's Church, said Mrs. Dalrymple, had there been a scandal like unto this.

"But there's *no* scandal," he pleaded. "Rose is married, for heaven's sake. She and Jim have been married for twelve years, as you know very well."

Mrs. Dalrymple bit her lip. "That's just it," she said stiffly. "It's unseemly." And once again the wave of red crawled up under the black felt hat.

"Think of Joachim and Anne, Zachary and Elizabeth," said Father Mackey, wildly dipping into Scripture for support, even though Rose was only thirty-seven. "Call it a blessed miracle, if you like, but *not* a scandal. And I," here he drew a deep breath, hoping that God would understand and forgive him, "am counting on *your*—er—womanly charity and Christian influence to set the right—um—attitude in the parish. And perhaps you might even crochet some ecru booties for Rose, to show her how pleased you are? Maybe that shell pattern, hmmm?"

The crafty seed fell on stony ground.

"A baby. A baby in St. Anthony's rectory," repeated Mrs. Dalrymple in unbelieving tones. She stood there, with her hand on the doorknob, as if waiting for God—with a single well-timed stroke of lightning—to demolish the rectory, thus terminating the whole unseemly business.

Father Mackey, who at this point would not have been averse to some well-timed lightning himself, could fairly see the images running through her mind. Weren't they still running through *his*? A playpen in the backyard, diapers waving in the breeze on the clothesline. Not to mention the wailing that would undoubtedly shatter the wee small hours, even though Rose and Jim had a room way to the back.

The one redeeming feature, as it applied here, was that

this was a poor parish, on the wrong side of the tracks, and
the parishioners—mostly mill hands—had a down to earth
approach. The playpen in the backyard wouldn't seem *quite*
so preposterous as it would, say, at St. James' Church over
in Shorewood Heights.

Even so, it was still as unnerving a prospect as had ever
faced a new, and young, and untried-by-fire pastor. Worse,
there was nothing in canon law that indicated a clear-cut course
of action. *This* was a dilemma that had never arisen even in
a seminarian bull session.

Yet if the prospect of the baby dismayed him, and it did,
the prospect of the alternative dismayed him more: to kick
Rose and Jim out on the street, without a job and during
a housing shortage, and then—like Pilate—to wash his
hands. Did their long and honorable tenure, as housekeeper
and janitor, count for nothing? Moreover, he had heard just
enough plaintive moans from other pastors to realize that, in
Rose, he had found a valiant woman, a jewel without price.

"Look, Mrs. Dalrymple," he said, in a last-ditch plea, "let's
agree that this is rather an unusual and even unconventional
situation. Yet even Emily Post, not to mention St. Paul, says
that the *charitable* way is always the right way, when in doubt.
Why not go as far as we can—doing what's right, that is,
according to our lights—and not try to solve tomorrow's problems with today's graces?"

The editorial "we" carried no appeal. Mrs. Dalrymple
appeared as responsive as a stone gargoyle.

Gazing desperately around him, like a drowning man
clutching for a straw, Father Mackey suddenly spied his
straw.

"Look, Mrs. Dalrymple," he said, eagerly trying a lighter

vein, "we *already* have a baby in the rectory. It hasn't caused any particular trouble, has it, now?"

He pointed to the four-foot statue, resting on an oak pedestal in one corner of the vestibule, of the Infant of Prague. He had been able to pick it up cheap because of its broken right arm, but it was still a fine statue with its real satin cape, encrusted with imitation gems, and its gilt detachable crown. The kids in the parish loved it. Even now, there was a forgotten red mitten lying at its feet, a mitten that some kid had removed in order to finger the row of colored "jewels."

"The Christ Child doesn't always come in a white satin cape, you know," he began, suddenly struck with the possibility of driving home a poignant parallel, and then he stopped. The stone gargoyle was in no mood for poignant parallels.

"So this is final?" she asked. It was the tossing down of the gauntlet and he knew it. Up to now she had merely resented him, but this was open warfare; the quick end of his dream of becoming the beloved shepherd.

"Quite final," said Father Mackey. As he closed the door behind her, he did not feel the wonderful sense of relief he had been anticipating all evening. Instead, he felt a stab of desolation and fear. His enemy, going out into the night, would immediately start sowing tares among his wheat. All that he would probably have left, among the wheat, would be his Cub Scouts. These were the green shoots, and he treasured them, but he also wanted the ripe wheat and the bent wheat and even the old dry hollow stalks. Yet it was possible for this one woman, with her far-reaching influence, to start. . . .

"I like parish life," he said under his breath. "I like parish life, I like parish life. . . ."

Reciting his litany, he walked through the living room

—with its worn rug, golden oak furniture, and stiff lace cur-
tains—and on out into the kitchen. But he knew it wasn't
the litany in his heart. *That* litany went: "I want them to like
me, I want them to like me. . . ."

He knew that it showed a human weakness: this caring
what they thought of him, this wanting to be accepted, this
wanting to be—yes!—popular. All that should matter, in a
case of right or wrong, was God's opinion but, doggone it,
how could he get close to these people if they wouldn't let
him? If only. . . .

If *only* old Father Kennedy had been transferred to the
nun's infirmary in June, as had been slated, instead of suddenly dying of pneumonia in April! It wasn't easy to step into
the shoes of someone who, by death, had immediately achieved
the status of a canonized saint in the eyes of his parishioners.
Not that Father Kennedy might not have been a saint, of
course. Come to think of it, he probably *was* after all these
years of putting up with Mrs. Dalrymple. Perhaps death
had even come as a pleasant surprise?

He decided to make a bacon sandwich. Opening the refrigerator, he discovered, to his dismay, that there *was* no
bacon. Well, then, a bowl of corn flakes, but it seemed sorry
fare for a man who had just put in an evening such as he had.
He reached for the bottle of cream and then noticed the rubber jar ring around it: Rose's official warning that it was
sour. Well, then, skimmed milk and corn flakes.

"I suffer uniquely and intensely," he announced aloud,
remembering the line from Bloy that they had always kicked
around, with mock martyrdom, in the seminary.

Sitting at the white-topped table, eating his corn flakes, he
found himself idly reading the advertising on the side of the
Kellogg's box. For only twenty cents and the box top, he could

get an "F-87" super jet plane ring with a secret launching trigger that would amaze all the kids in the neighborhood.

Well, he was going to amaze all the kids in the neighborhood *without* owning an "F-87" super jet plane ring. Just wait until his confrères, especially Bill over at Holy Name, found out there would be a baby in the rectory, come June. He could imagine, without half trying, all the corny gags on baby tending he'd have to put up with.

But he wouldn't mind the ribbing so much (he'd had more than his quota during his first year as a teacher, trying to teach Church History) if only they wouldn't *really* think he was doing the wrong thing. That is, wrong in the sense that he was stepping out of line and following conviction rather than tradition. That had always been the good-natured charge against him: letting his fine Christian principles, that he took very seriously and literally, override prudence. (He, they said, was the sort of chap who, if a man asked for his coat, would immediately start unbuttoning it.) Yes, he and prudence had tangled before . . .

"It's all very well," Father Boyle, his spiritual director, had once said, "to go around restoring all things in Christ but *you* always upset so much in the process." But Father Boyle had also said something else, in one of his milder moods: "Don't let them change you, Mac. People have a way of hiding a lot of sins—like sweeping the dust under the rug or powdering a dirty neck—and calling it prudence."

Father Mackey picked up his bowl and spoon, walked over to the sink, and let the cold water run over them. Then he put them, along with the Kellogg's box, carefully away in the cupboard. Rose always worried, in her gentle way, that she wasn't feeding him enough when she found the tell-tale marks of his refrigerator raidings.

He lit a cigarette and then pulled out the letter he'd received that morning from Joe Givern out on the Gold Coast. It made exciting reading, even for the third time. Joe was really fighting the good fight: baptizing pagan souls right and left, and having hardships and adventures that made St. Paul's shipwrecks look pretty tame. *He* wasn't just reading about super jet planes on the backs of corn flakes boxes, but was really amazing the kids in the neighborhood. One day he had even had to shoot a panther. It was only a *small* panther, Joe had added scrupulously, and not worth mounting because it hadn't been a clean shot. But the native had said it was a vicious. . . .

Suddenly, from behind the pantry door, came a loud, familiar snap. With a little sigh, Father Mackey stubbed out his cigarette and went into the pantry to administer last rites. Fishing around behind some coke bottles, he pulled out the mousetrap he had set that morning. It was a clean shot. The mouse, without a single drop of blood on its soft grey neck, hung limp on its wooden bier.

Father Mackey carried his game out on the back steps, carefully sidestepping the milk bottles, and deposited it in the garbage can. Somehow, it seemed a fitting climax—this killing a mouse—to an evening devoted to Mrs. Dalrymple's asthma and ecru tablecloth, Miss Cronk and the health board, the cracked window shades . . .

All of which, he thought, would certainly make exciting and edifying reading in his next letter to Joe. Timothy, with his schoolboy letter of insignificant odds and ends, writing back to St. Paul! Oh, he knew, of course, that purity of intention could make even the odds and ends a mighty fulcrum to lift the world: "Pick up a pin for the love of God," St. Thérèse had said, "and you may save a soul." He knew, too, that personal sanctity wasn't a glamorous, swashbuckling dash up Mount Carmel: more often, it consisted of just putting one foot ahead of the other, understanding nothing. Yet he couldn't help feeling, just the same, that . . .

Putting the lid firmly back on the garbage pail, he straightened up—the empty mousetrap dangling from his fingers—and stared soberly up at the dark sky. There was only a faint sprinkling of stars; nothing, certainly, to plunge him into rapt contemplation, but there was a mild clean freshness in the air that was unusual for February.

As he stood there on the back steps, deeply and consciously inhaling and exhaling, it reminded him of the old Boy Scout formula for resuscitation: "*Out* goes the bad air, *in* comes the good." *Out* goes Mrs. Dalrymple and his bid for parish popularity, *in* comes—well, what? Grace, maybe? The grace to go as far as you could each day and then, come night, just to exhale and let Divine Providence take over?

For no particular good reason, he suddenly felt lighthearted again as he went back into the kitchen and reset his mousetrap. As he shoved it back behind the pantry door, he found himself grinning. It was only a *small* mouse, he could write Joe, and hardly worth mounting, but it *had* been a clean shot.